STAFFORDSHIRE PORTRAIT FIGURES
OF THE VICTORIAN AGE

[1.] Prince Albert and Napoleon III 2u

STAFFORDSHIRE
PORTRAIT FIGURES
OF THE
VICTORIAN AGE

by

THOMAS BALSTON

FABER AND FABER LIMITED

24 Russell Square

London

First published in mcmlviii
by Faber and Faber Limited
24 Russell Square London W.C.1
Printed in Great Britain by
R. MacLehose and Company Limited
The University Press Glasgow

Acknowledgements

This attempt to make a thorough survey of Victorian Staffordshire Portrait Figures would have been impossible without the enthusiastic collaboration of the many other collectors with whom I have become acquainted in the last eight years. The first were Messrs Raymond Mander and Joe Mitchenson, the founders of the theatrical collection well-known to all students of the stage. They had already for many years been collecting and recording theatrical figures, and in 1944 they had made the valuable discovery that seven Shakespearean figures were based on engravings in Tallis's *Shakespeare Gallery* (1852–3), and from the lettering on the engravings had proved that these figures were not imaginary representations of Shakespearean characters but portraits of actual actors. And further, by studying the style of these figures, they had identified many other figures as coming from the same factory. To their kindness in keeping me informed of their researches I am deeply indebted, especially in the theatrical section of my Catalogue and in my account of the 'Tallis' factory.

Second, in point of time, were Mr and Mrs E. H. Joyce. When we met they were already enthusiastic collectors, and within the next few years they had made their collection the largest in the country. From an early date they encouraged me to write this book, and ever since they have given me unstinted assistance. At many meetings, and in innumerable letters we have discussed every problem. On many questions of dating and identification they have corrected my ideas, and they have kept me informed of the many rare pieces which they have secured or seen in every part of England, of which otherwise I would never have heard. Thanks to them I can now hope that my Catalogue is as nearly complete as such a pioneer work can be.

Other collectors who have kindly assisted by showing me their collections are Mrs Cecil Woodham-Smith, Mrs H. de C. Hastings, Mrs Hugh McCorquodale, Mrs Gerald Legge, Mr and Mrs Don Atkins, the Hon. G. C. Chubb, Mr Bryan Latham, Dr S. J. Howard, Mr Theodore Smythe, Sir Gerard d'Erlanger, Mr Arthur Tite, Mr John Arlott, Mr C. A. Vandervell and Mr P. D. Power. I have also received valuable information about figures in their possession from Mr R. Shockledge, Sir G. Tyrwhitt-Drake, Mrs Burton, Mr J. Homery Folkes, Mr Doherty Bellock, and Mr T. C. Pepper.

ACKNOWLEDGEMENTS

Many years ago I was much encouraged by the late Mr H. L. Parr's appreciation of the figures bequeathed by Dr Glaisher to the Fitzwilliam Museum, and by his interest in my own collection. More recently I received encouragement from Mr Derek Rogers of the Brighton Museum, Mr George Naish of the National Maritime Museum, Mr Geoffrey Bemrose of the Hanley Museum, Miss Diana Kerr of Lords, and the staff of the Ceramics Department of the Victoria and Albert Museum. I am also very grateful to Miss Sarah Pugh Jones of Llangollen who took much trouble to supply me with evidence which led to the identification of 'Edward Morgan'.

For the chapters on the processes of manufacture and colouring I am deeply indebted to Mr Peter O'Malley of the Royal College of Art, who spared no pains to give me all the information I required, and to make sure that I understood it.

My visits to the Potteries were made pleasant and profitable by Mr T. Fox and Mr T. Wright of Sampson Smith's and Mr D. C. Hall of William Kent, Ltd, who found time to show me over their Works and answer my many questions.

The photographing of 266 figures for the Plates presented a complicated problem. No one collection contained all the pieces which it was desirable to reproduce, but it was essential that as many as possible should be photographed in groups, and that figures made in pairs or series should be grouped together. The problem was largely solved by Mr and Mrs Joyce who arranged fifteen groups from their collection to be photographed in their house, and also lent me seven pieces belonging to series which could more easily be completed in London. Many pieces were lent me by other collectors, twelve by Mr Bryan Latham, four by Mr Theodore Smythe, three by Sir Gerard d'Erlanger, two by Mrs Woodham-Smith, and six by Messrs Mander & Mitchenson (Jenny Lind 134a, c, and e, Shylock 127b, Lady Macbeth 135a, and Richard the Third 125a). All these loans were of rare pieces which I had never succeeded in acquiring, and I deeply appreciate the kindness and courage of the lenders in trusting such treasures to my care. Photographs of five essential figures which could not be brought to London were kindly supplied by Mrs Hastings and Mr Shockledge.

Finally Mr and Mrs Joyce have crowned their invaluable assistance by most carefully checking the proofs.

Flat 64
3 Whitehall Court
S.W.1

Contents

CONTENTS

Illustrations

11

ILLUSTRATIONS

CHAPTER ONE

Introductory

About thirty-five years ago I was given 'The Fortune Teller', a beautiful, highly coloured Staffordshire figure of the Victorian period. This led me to notice these figures in shops, and gradually to acquire some. I soon learnt from dealers that thousands were being exported, especially to the United States, and I determined to collect as many good pieces as I could, so that, when they came to be appreciated, there would be at least one representative collection of them in the country of their origin. But I soon discovered that the field was too wide for any one man's effort, and reluctantly I had to renounce whole classes of them (cottages, animals, and purely decorative pieces), and concentrate on one class only, the portrait figures. Neither I nor, I think, anyone else had then any idea that so large a number of portraits existed, but I soon found that I must confine my collection to contemporary or historical persons of whose physical appearance there was some record, and exclude imaginary representations of characters in books and plays, or of historical persons, such as those of the Bible, whose lineaments are unknown. I included, however, a small number of non-portrait figures, such as the Crimean fortresses and murderers' houses, because they throw light on the public's reaction to contemporary affairs.

Since 1951, when I published an article on my collection in *Country Life Annual*, I have learnt how essential these limits are. Other collectors have informed me of so many pieces which have eluded me that the number recorded in my Catalogue (chap. IX) has swollen to more than 470, representing more than 170 persons. Inevitably some more rarities will be discovered, but in the last few years the country has been so well combed by dealers and collectors that they are unlikely to be many.

For three hundred years pottery figures have been made in Staffordshire, and of those made in pre-Victorian times many specimens can be seen in museums throughout the country. Of the more popular figures, however, which began to appear in large numbers soon after the Queen's accession, very few are exhibited even temporarily, except some in the Willett Collection of the Brighton Art Gallery and in one case in the Victoria and Albert Museum.

INTRODUCTORY

The earliest appreciation of these later figures is found in Sir Herbert Read's *Staffordshire Pottery Figures*, published in 1929:

'Somewhere about 1840–50 there appears a new group of figures which have a very decided quality of their own. These figures are full of unconscious artistry. The attempt to compete with porcelain has been abandoned; the treatment is broad; the colouring restrained, but lively. They represent something free and independent in spirit, and something which was not destined to survive for long against the ubiquity of counterfeit or industrial art.'

In a later paragraph Sir Herbert paid tribute to the best potters of this period and of earlier good periods:

'The potter who made the figure was himself a peasant with a simple mind and a simple sense of humour. But because of this simple sense he often strays unconsciously into a realm of purer forms. He blunders into beauty, and it is the simplicity and sincerity of the potter's vision which has caused this miracle. All true peasant art is of this type; we can find the same qualities in the French painter, Henri Rousseau "Le Douanier", a man of much the same social standing as these Staffordshire potters, and a genius whose sense of beauty was equally unaffected by academic influences.'

A quarter of a century earlier, in 1903, Dr Glaisher, one of the greatest collectors of porcelain and earthenware, discovered merit in these Victorian figures, and began, with some hesitation, to collect them. He recorded his purchases, generally with some comment, in his manuscript Diary, now in the Fitzwilliam Museum, and occasionally stated the principles on which he bought:

'In buying Staffordshire figures of late date (say, after 1830) I only take those with a name or representing a known person or place, or which can be dated. Any such piece belongs to the class of "speaking pottery", and is historically interesting and worth procuring. It is also ceramically interesting when the date can be fixed.'

It was encouraging to discover, when I read this Diary, that I had been collecting for nearly twenty years on the same principles as such an expert.

When he died in 1928 about forty of these figures were included in his bequest to the Fitzwilliam. There they generally languish in a locked cupboard, but for a short time after the last war, pending the return of the Museum's porcelain, Mr H. L. Parr filled two of the principal show-cases at the top of the main stairway with an impressive selection. This was probably the finest display that these figures have yet received.

CHAPTER TWO

General Survey

The Victorian figures are distinguished from earlier Staffordshire figures by the greater whiteness of their clay and glaze, by their subsidiary parts being moulded and not hand-made, by more use of gold in their titling and decoration, and, for the first twenty years of their vogue, by the richness of their colouring, especially of the blue underglaze passages which are found on most of them. A further important distinction after the first few years is that most of the designers had given up any attempt to imitate porcelain, and had taken to larger and simpler designs which could be much more effectively reproduced in earthenware.

1840–5

The genesis of this new kind of figures synchronised with a unique event in English history, the wedding of a young Queen; the earliest that can be dated with certainty are the seated pair of the Queen (1c) and Prince Albert (2a) who were married in February 1840. In November of that year the Princess Royal was born, and many pairs were made of the Queen and Albert in which she is holding a baby in long clothes. A year later, in November 1841, the Prince of Wales was born, and the seated pair of the Queen with the Princess (1v) and Albert with the Prince (2r), with both children wearing short skirts, must date from 1842–3. Then or within the next two or three years innumerable other figures were made of the children, with or without their parents. Many of the small mounted figures of the Queen and Albert may also belong to this period.

Meanwhile a few dateable non-royal figures were appearing; Sir Robert and Lady Sale in 1842, Pilch and Box in 1843, and the two figures of Jemmy Wood at some date from 1840 to 1844. Figures which are certainly Victorian but may date from before the Queen's marriage are Van Amburgh (*Pl.* 48) and Grace Darling. The former is in a pre-Victorian style, with its many subsidiary parts modelled by hand.

Nearly all the figures of this period are small, richly coloured, and of complicated designs, and show no recognisable likeness to their subjects, but both the figures of

Jemmy Wood are made from single two-piece moulds, and closely resemble his woodcut portraits.

1846–53

By 1846 the public appear to have lost interest in the royal children; there are no known figures of the seven younger children in childhood and, except for two of the Prince of Wales (5c & d), none of him or the Princess Royal till late in the fifties. Most however of the larger single figures of the Queen and Albert are likely to belong to this period, many of them perhaps inspired by the opening of the Great Exhibition in 1851. But the salient feature of this short period is that it was the only one which produced a large number of portraits of non-royal civilians in many walks of life. Among them were at least a dozen different models of the Duke of Wellington, most of them in civilian clothes as the revered Elder Statesman; six of Peel and two of Cobden celebrated the Repeal of the Corn Laws, two represented the philanthropist Lord Shaftesbury and one each the Chartist Thomas Duncombe, the explorer Sir John Franklin and his wife, and the poetess Eliza Cook. Music and the Stage produced nine of Jenny Lind, one of Jullien, and many of Macready and other actors. In 1848 and 1849 crime had its greatest vogue with figures of William Smith O'Brien and his wife, of J. B. Rush and Emily Sandford, and of F. G. and Maria Manning. In 1851 the visit of Kossuth, the Hungarian patriot, inspired three figures, and that of Mrs Bloomer, the American dress-reformer, two. In this period also many figures were made of many great men of the past, of Cranmer, Ridley and Latimer, inspired by the 'No Popery' agitation of 1851, of the writers Burns, Byron and Scott, and of the explorer Captain Cook.

Nearly all the figures of this period have most of their surface coloured, and show some likeness to their subjects. Most of them were made by the 'Alpha' and 'Tallis' factories, of whom an account will be found in the next chapter. Both these factories persisted, with considerable success, in the attempt to imitate porcelain, and generally worked from models which require at least two or three subsidiary moulds. Some other factories, however, had begun to employ larger and broader designs with the softer outlines more appropriate to earthenware. The earliest that can be definitely dated are the figures of the Mannings and of Rush and Emily Sandford which belong to 1849, but some other figures of this kind, of the Duke and Duchess of Cambridge, King Leopold of the Belgians, and the Duke of Wellington, may be a few years earlier. The Mannings were made from single two-piece moulds, and none of the others required more than one or two subsidiaries. They could be made at less expense than the more elaborate figures, and this must

[2.] Wellington 20i — O'Connell 12a

have helped them to capture the market. After 1853 only very few new models were made of any other kind.

1854–5

The outbreak of the Crimean War in February 1854 aroused intense popular enthusiasm, and created an unprecedented demand for Staffordshire figures, especially for portraits of the allied sovereigns and their chief commanders. Within the next eighteen months figures were made of the Queen with each of her allies, Napoleon III, the Sultan, and the King of Sardinia, of Albert with Napoleon, and many of the Sultan and Napoleon and the Empress Eugénie. At least two English Admirals and one Turkish, three French, and eight English Generals were portrayed, many of them in two or more models, and many of the models in two or three sizes; and there were three of Florence Nightingale. Besides all these portraits there were representations of three Russian fortresses, and an incalculable number of British and Allied soldiers and sailors. Many of them, though they are not portraits, I have included in my Catalogue, both on account of their interest as records of the popular enthusiasm and of their excellence as figures.

With the single exception of 'Success to Turkey', a portrait of Omar Pasha from the 'Tallis' factory, all the recorded portrait figures are in the new broader style, most of them flat-backed.

1856–64

The Indian Mutiny of 1857 produced portraits of Havelock, Colin Campbell, and Highland Jessie, and the threat of a French invasion in 1860 produced one of the new Volunteer Rifles and one of the British Lion couched on top of a French officer, presumably Napoleon III (66a).

Among the figures of the Queen and Albert to which no date can be definitely assigned there seems to be none in a style which indicates that it dates from after the Crimean War; certainly none records the prematurely aged appearance of Albert in these years, or shows any connection with his death in 1861. (It is possible that the single figure of the Queen with a lion (Pl. 12) synchronised with the Napoleon beneath a lion.) But there was some revival of interest in the royal children. Figures were made of the Princess Royal and Prince Frederick William for their marriage in 1858, and some of the Prince of Wales and Prince Alfred in 1859 when they received their first commissions in the Army and Navy. A pair of the Princess Alice and Prince Louis of Hesse commemorates their marriage in 1862. Rumours of plans for the Prince of Wales's marriage early in 1862 may have caused the production of his fine single figure in civilian dress (5g), but this was followed by a spate of figures of him and the Princess Alexandra after their engagement was announced in September.

Before and after the Prince's marriage the public was much interested in the American Civil War (1861–5). Only two portraits resulted, Abraham Lincoln and John Brown, but the public's intense sympathy with the North is shown by the very many figures made of the chief characters in *Uncle Tom's Cabin*, which may have been made at any date since its publication here in 1852.

The war was still continuing when Garibaldi's arrival here in 1864 aroused the last great demand for any one person's portrait. At least a dozen models were made of him, most of them in more than one size; among them were the 19″ standing figure (*Pl.* 9), the tallest known portrait, and the 15″ one of him leaning against his horse, the most elaborate and expensive figure made by the 'Tallis' factory.

The market for portraits of contemporaries who were neither royal nor military had been extinguished by the Crimean War, and was never much revived. During this period of nine years the only dateable portraits of an eminent civilian were two of Spurgeon, but a few others were inspired by crimes, sport or entertainments; Palmer, the Rugeley poisoner, in 1856; Rarey, the American horse-tamer, and Heenan and Sayers, the boxers, in 1860; Sothern as Lord Dundreary in 1861; and Frank Gardiner, the Australian bushranger, in 1864.

Except for four figures of Garibaldi and one of Victor Emmanuel, King of Italy (formerly of Sardinia), all made by the 'Tallis' factory, the portrait figures of this period are in the broader style. From its start in the later forties many figures in this style are found both highly coloured and also much more sparsely, with little but their hair, faces, hands and shoes painted, though always with some gilt decoration on their white parts.[1] As early as the Crimean War some figures, e.g. the tall standing figures of Windham and Simpson (*Pl.* 24), have only been found in the paler state. By the sixties, judging by the numbers of each sort which have survived, it seems that the market preferred the paler ones.

1865–9

In these five years after Garibaldi's visit the art seems almost extinct. No figures have been found in connection with the marriage of the Queen's third daughter,

---

[1] Some collectors are led by their preference for the coloured pieces to consider that they are the earlier, and that it was only when the market was declining that the potters economised in the painting. Whiter pieces however are found no less sharp than the coloured. This may be because, though later, they were made from fresh working-moulds, but it seems probable that by the fifties the potters were making both sorts simultaneously, being aware that the public's taste was changing.

the Princess Helena, to Prince Christian of Schleswig-Holstein in 1866. The 'Tallis' figure of Lord Napier of Magdala (*Pl.* 47) made in 1867 is the only new portrait model of these years, and that is only a copy in reverse, with little alteration, of a smaller size of the same firm's Garibaldi (69g) of 1864.

1870–80

In 1870 some revival was produced by the Franco-German War; figures were made of the King, Queen, Crown Prince, and Prince Frederick Charles of Prussia and of Moltke and Bismarck on the German side, and of Bazaine and MacMahon on the French. Probably all these were made between July 15th, when the war started with much pro-German feeling in this country, and September 19th, when the Germans invested Paris, and much popular sympathy went over to France. Those of the King and Queen were certainly made before January 1871, when their titles changed to Emperor and Empress of Germany.

In the next four years there was some revival of interest in the Royal Family. In 1871 a pair were made for the marriage of the Queen's fourth daughter, the Princess Louise, to the Marquess of Lorne, and in 1874 for the marriage of the Duke of Edinburgh (Prince Alfred) to the Grand Duchess Marie of Russia. The monumental model of the Queen which was revived with appropriate inscriptions for her Jubilees in 1887 and 1897, and its companion, the bearded Prince of Wales, are also likely to date from the early 1870's.[1]

Figures were also made of four religionists, Moody and Sankey (not before 1873) and the Pope and Manning (not before 1875), and of two statesmen, the first since the forties, Beaconsfield and Gladstone (not before 1876).

There was also some revival of figures inspired by crime, sport, and entertainment; in 1871 the greyhounds 'McGrath' and 'Pretender', in 1873 Orton, the Tichborne Claimant, and 'Have you seen the Shah', after a music hall song about the visit of Nasr-ed-Din, and in 1875 Captain Webb, the first swimmer of the Channel. 'Jumbo', the African elephant, who was the popular favourite at the Zoo from 1865 to 1882, may also belong to these years.

By 1870, when this revival started, underglaze blue had almost, if not entirely, ceased to be used on these figures. All the Franco-Prussian War and Royal figures of this period are predominantly white, with only a little pale tinting and some gilding, except that a stronger orange is found on the pedestals of the Prince of Wales and the Duke of Edinburgh. In the later seventies black, generally underglaze, was much used on the clothing of civilian figures, and strong colours on pedestals and

---

[1] See Ch. VIII for the reasons for dating these two figures from about 1872.

backgrounds. The only figure of this period found almost entirely painted is the Tichborne Claimant.

The outstanding feature of this period is the group of monumental figures, 16" to 17½" high, all probably made by Sampson Smith.[1] Though less firmly modelled than the large figures of earlier periods, most of them are still attractive as honest attempts by their designers to cope with their problems in a new way.

1880–1901

By 1880 the art was dying, but the trade survived for twenty-two more years. Some artistry may still be found in the Generals of the Egyptian Wars (1882–1885), but none in those of the River War (1896–8) and the South African War (1899–1902); the Jubilees of 1887 and 1897 only produced debased copies of the earlier figures of the Queen and Prince of Wales; and two graceless figures marked the engagement of the Duke of Clarence and the Princess May (Queen Mary) in 1891. Further figures of Gladstone and two of Parnell were made in the eighties, and the deplorable cast figures of Mr and Mrs Gladstone in the nineties.

For their historical interest alone all these figures have been included in my Catalogue. There is however one bright spot in this period, the life-size bust of General Booth (*Pl.* 4). The great white beard suggests that it was not made earlier than the nineties, since he was only born in 1829. Both in its size and in being a cast figure it differs from all other good portrait figures of the Victorian era, and it is the only portrait with underglaze blue which must be dated later than 1863. Other collectors agree with me in thinking that it is essentially in the tradition of this folk art, but it is likely to have been made in special circumstances, perhaps a private commission, which inspired the potter to make such a large, elaborate, and faithful portrait.

AFTERMATH

For eighteen months after the Queen's death in January 1901, hideous figures continued to be made, some of King Edward and Queen Alexandra to celebrate their succession and their Coronation, and one to celebrate Victory in the South African War. When portrait figures reappeared twelve years later in the First World War, they were of a very different and more sophisticated kind.

It is clear from the above review that throughout our period it was war alone that always produced a market for these figures; every major war in which the country

[1] See Ch. III.

was engaged produced its quota, and others were inspired by the American Civil War and the Franco-German War. A second great interest was in the Royal Family, but this almost ceased after the early seventies; during the last twenty-eight years of the Queen's reign no new model appears to have been made of her or the Prince of Wales.

Both these groups had a nation-wide appeal, but two smaller groups, of politicians and religionists, show a marked Liberal and Nonconformist bias. Of right-wing politicians Beaconsfield alone is represented, and only as a pair to his great rival, while to the left, besides a number of independent figures of Gladstone, there are Peel and Cobden to celebrate the Repeal of the Corn Laws, Duncombe the Chartist, Gurney and Shaftesbury the philanthropists, O'Connell and Parnell. The same democratic bias is shown by the enthusiasm for Kossuth and Garibaldi, and by the making of portraits of Lord Edward Fitzgerald, Wolfe Tone, and McCracken to commemorate the centenary of the Irish Rebellion of 1798. The sympathy with the North in the American Civil War and with Prussia at the beginning of the Franco-Prussian War was most common among Liberals, and even the Crimean War was so popular because it was fought against an autocrat.

The Nonconformist bias is even more conspicuous. If, as seems probable, the figure entitled 'Coulburn' really represents Dr Goulburn, it is the only known portrait of a cleric of the Church of England; the untitled figure in cassock, surplice and bands, which was thought to be Church of England (possibly Charles Simeon) has now been found with the title 'Dr Raffles', an Independent minister. On the other hand at least a dozen were made of Nonconformist preachers ranging from Wesley to Moody and Sankey.

There are some surprising blanks in the Catalogue. No figures have been found, for instance, of Palmerston, the most popular minister of the Crimean War, of Dickens, whose works were read throughout the Queen's reign by nearly everybody who could read, or of Tennyson, who became Poet Laureate in 1850 and, after the publication of the *Idylls of the King* in 1859, was immensely popular. If figures had been made of them, they would surely have sold in large numbers, and many copies would now survive, but this chapter has shown how very spasmodic was the output of portrait figures, and how very few were made of eminent civilians after 1852.

CHAPTER THREE

The Manufacturers

No reason has been found to doubt the tradition that a vast majority of the so-called Staffordshire Figures were made there, though some, as will be seen, were made in Scotland, and others probably in Wales. Mr R. G. Haggar, in his *Staffordshire Chimney Ornaments*, gives the names of many firms which made 'toys' or 'figures' in the Five Towns during our period, but, as none of our earlier pieces and very few later ones bear makers' marks, it is only to two firms, Sampson Smith's and Lancaster's, that any pieces can be definitely attributed. There were however two unidentified firms producing pieces with very individual characteristics; for the sake of convenience I propose to call them the 'Alpha' factory and the 'Tallis' factory.

At least twenty-three figures, all sitting or standing, can be readily recognised as the products of one (the 'Alpha') factory. Two are 7½" figures of Jesus Christ and the Virgin Mary, but the rest are portraits of contemporaries or of historical persons whose features are on record, and are all to be seen on *Plates* 7 and 46:

Queen Victoria	Sir John Franklin	Eliza Cook
Prince of Wales	Lady Franklin	Mrs Bloomer (2 figs.)
Princess Royal	Jenny Lind (2 figs.)	Captain Cook
Peel (2 figs.)	Jullien	Burns
Cobden	W. S. O'Brien	Byron
Shaftesbury	Mrs O'Brien	Voltaire

All the contemporaries can be confidently dated from 1845 to 1851, and the historical figures are so similar in style that they are likely to be of the same period. All are modelled and painted all round (there are no flat-backs among them), and are so complicated in design as to require at least three moulds, Captain Cook, the most complicated, requiring eight. Sixteen of them are titled with indented capitals, with a gilt leaf or three strokes of gold paint at each end of the lettering; the others have a gilt line half way up across the front of the base and descending to the bottom of the base on each side.[1] All except the two Franklins and Eliza Cook, which are

[1] Some, perhaps later, copies of Jenny Lind (134f) and Jullien have been found with their titles not indented but in gilt script between three gilt strokes.

22

likely to be the latest of the group, are found with underglaze blue passages. All are of white porcelaneous clay, and are so well modelled, moulded, and painted that they are frequently offered for sale as Rockingham.

There are other pieces, especially among the small royal figures of the early forties, which have many of the characteristics of this group, and may have been made by this factory before it perfected its technique.

The other factory is here called the 'Tallis' factory because, among the figures attributed to it, are the seven with Shakespearean titles which were found by Messrs Mander and Mitchenson to be based on engravings in Tallis' *Shakespeare Gallery* (1852–3):

'Alas, poor Yorick' (Kemble as Hamlet)	*Plate* 45
Falstaff (J. H. Hackett)	*Plate* 45
Shylock (Macready)	*Plate* 45
Macbeth (Macready)	*Plate* 45
Lady Macbeth (Isabella Glyn)	*Plate* 45
Romeo and Juliet (Charlotte and Susan Cushman)	*Plate* 16
Winter's Tale (F. Robinson and Jenny Marston)	*Plate* 16

There is also an 'Ophelia' (*Pl.* 45) in the series, but no corresponding engraving, and there are two very similar figures of non-Shakespearean characters, 'Harlequin' and 'Columbine'. Probably none of these portrays an individual actor.

Study of the characteristics of these figures has led to the attribution of many others to the 'Tallis' factory, and among them are the following portraits:

c. 1849	Prince of Wales, after Winterhalter (*Pl.* 11)
184–	Wellington, 'Up, Guards, and at them' (*Pl.* 16)
1851	Cranmer (*Pl.* 38). Ridley and Latimer (*Pl.* 38)
1854	Omar Pasha, 'Success to Turkey' (*Pl.* 26)
1862	Prince of Wales (*Pl.* 38). Princess (*Pl.* 38)
1864	Garibaldi (69e, f, g, h)
1864	Victor Emmanuel (33d)
1867	Lord Napier of Magdala (*Pl.* 47)
1884	Gordon (*Pl.* 50)

The 'Tallis' figures have the following characteristics:
(1) They are made of an exceptionally hard and heavy body.
(2) They are both modelled and painted all round.

(3) Their bases are coloured with brown and green, 'combed' in long, thin strokes, sometimes with the addition of a little pale orange.

(4) They have no underglaze colouring.

(5) Some have titles in indented caps., and some have titles and/or quotations in transfer, but none has raised caps. or gilt script. The Prince of Wales (*Pl.* 11), alone of the portraits, has no title or quotation.

The moulds of very many 'Tallis' figures, not only portraits, are now in the possession of William Kent (Porcelains) Ltd, by whom many of them are still employed. This firm was not founded till 1878, and therefore cannot be the original makers of the portrait figures except Gordon, since the others all date from 1849 to 1867.[1]

Most of the figures of the 'Alpha' and 'Tallis' factories have the firm and meticulous modelling more commonly found in porcelain, but by 1849 at the latest some other factory was working with broader designs more appropriate for earthenware. The great murder trials of that year are commemorated by the figures of F. G. and Maria Manning and of Rush and Emily Sandford (*Pl.* 48) which differ from the work of the 'Alpha' and 'Tallis' factories in this respect, and also by their flat backs and gilt-script titles. Their style suggests that they were early works of Sampson Smith.

Sampson Smith (*b.* 1813) worked at Longton from about 1846 till his death in 1878; in 1851 his factory was in Upper High Street, but in 1859 he moved to the Sutherland Works in Barker Street, where Barker Bros Ltd still operate under his name. In the *Post Office Directory* for 1860 he appears as a maker of figures for home and exportation, and in the *Mercantile Directory of the Pottery District* for 1864 he advertised that he made figures in great variety. Till recently, although there was a tradition that he was the chief maker of these figures,[2] only a few dogs, bearing his mark, could be identified as his, but in 1948 the present firm discovered fifty or sixty old press-moulds in a disused part of the factory. Most of them were single two-part moulds, and among them, besides many dogs, cottages, jockeys, etc., there were the portraits of Wellington (20c) and Napoleon I (34a), Dick

---

[1] William Kent Ltd have kindly informed me that they do not know how they acquired the moulds. At some date they bought moulds from William Machin of Hanley, but he, according to Mr Haggar, flourished from 1875 to 1889, too late to have originated them.

Gaskell, Kent and Parr were the predecessors of William Kent Ltd in the works in Auckland Street (late Wellington Street), Burslem, which they have occupied ever since their foundation in 1878. One John Parr, already a maker of 'toys' in 1860, had moved into these works in 1875, and is likely to be the Parr in this partnership. There had been Parr 'toy'-makers at Burslem, Richard (*c.* 1828), William (*c.* 1860), and Edward (*c.* 1860–4). It may have been through their connection with the Parrs that the Kents acquired the moulds.

[2] In his *Catalogue of the Glaisher Collection* (1935) Mr Bernard Rackham listed all but two of Dr Glaisher's figures of this kind as 'of a type made chiefly by Sampson Smith's'.

[3.] Garibaldi 69a

Turpin (150b) and Tom King (151b), Burns, both with Highland Mary (118g) and alone (118f), and Moody (*Pl.* 42). The discovery of Moody was particularly fortunate, since it enabled six other figures (see *Pl.* 41 and 42) to be confidently attributed to Sampson Smith; Sankey, the pair to Moody, and the Pope, Cardinal Manning, O'Connell, Beaconsfield and Gladstone, since they closely resemble Moody and Sankey in many points:

(1) All seven are monumental standing figures, ranging from 16″ to 17½″ in height.

(2) All are on plain oval bases surmounted by rough ground, generally painted with a deep green mixed with some brown.

(3) All except Manning and the Pope are partly supported by stone walls; the skirts of Manning's soutane make such support unnecessary.

(4) All except the Pope are made from single two-part moulds; one subsidiary was needed for the Pope's arm raised in blessing.

(5) All are partly flat-back.

(6) All except Moody and Sankey have gilt-script titles of similar lettering; the titles of Moody and Sankey are in raised caps.

(7) All except the Pope and Manning are in civilian dress generally painted with underglaze black.

(8) All probably date between 1873, when Moody and Sankey first came to England, and 1881, when Beaconsfield died.

There are so many points of resemblance between these figures and the six monumental royal figures of 1870 to 1874[1] that there can be little doubt that they came from the same factory.

None of these figures can be dated earlier than 1870, but there are many figures of the forties, fifties, and sixties, large and small, standing and mounted, on plain (generally oval) bases titled with gilt-script or raised caps., which have a similar breadth and simplicity.[2] Even some which appear complicated are found to be so cleverly designed that they come from single moulds, e.g. the large group of Albert and Napoleon III (*Pl.* 1). In view of the tradition that Sampson Smith was the chief manufacturer of this period, it is not rash to surmise that they were all made by his firm.

Many figures have neither the broad design of Sampson Smith's nor the firm

---

[1] For their titles and a discussion of their dates see Ch. VIII.

[2] Among the most conspicuous are the large figures of the Prince of Wales with his dog (*Pl.* 11), Florence Nightingale (*Pl.* 31) and the two Cricketers (*Pl.* 25), and the large groups of the Prince with his Princess (*Pl.* 10), and Highland Jessie (*Pl.* 29). All these are from single moulds. For the large mounted figures of Garibaldi, Peard and Lincoln on *Plate* 34, a subsidiary mould was needed for one of the horse's legs. The 19″ Garibaldi (*Pl.* 3) also needed only one subsidiary, and the 18¼″ Shakespeare (114b) only two.

modelling of the 'Alpha' and 'Tallis' factories. Their varieties in style suggest that they were produced by many of the factories which then congested the Potteries, but it is possible to distinguish some small groups which must have come from the same factory. Perhaps the most conspicuous are two series, each of five mounted Crimean notabilities; one includes the figures of the Sultan, Omar Pasha, Saint-Arnaud, Raglan (*Pl. 26*), and the Duke of Cambridge (*Pl. 23*) with their names in raised caps. on shaped tablets, and the other, possibly from the same factory, larger and more flamboyant figures of Napoleon III, the Empress Eugénie and the Generals Brown, Simpson, and Pelissier (*Pl. 23*). Nearly all these ten need three subsidiary moulds (two for the near legs of the horse, and one for the near leg of the rider), with the result that they are fussier in design than the many similar mounted figures made (presumably by Sampson Smith) with only one subsidiary.

SCOTLAND

From the middle of the eighteenth century onwards potters, painters, and gilders from Staffordshire were constantly being imported into Scottish potteries, with the result that Scottish earthenware figures can seldom be distinguished from English. In his *Scottish Pottery* (1923) J. Arnold Fleming gave illustrations of eight figures of our period which he ascribed to Scottish potteries.[1] 'The Bower' (Plate XXV) and 'Prince Albert' and 'Victoria' (Plate XXVII), from the Victoria Pottery, Pollokshaws, appear to be crude, whitish copies of familiar English pieces, the two latter being identical with the Prince of Wales (5j) and Princess (6c). Four small decorative figures (Plate XL) from Rathbone's Pottery, Portobello, three of them highly coloured, are similar to many found in England. 'Fishwives' however (Plate XXXIII), from the Prestonpans Pottery, is a characteristic example of the many substantial, firmly moulded, and fully coloured figures of Newhaven fishergirls in their native dress, which have a marked individuality, and may be presumed to be of purely Scottish origin. Similar qualities are found in the three monumental portraits of Scottish national heroes, Wallace (191a), Bruce (192a), and Rob Roy (193a), and in a fourth, the legendary William Tell (194a), but I was informed at the Royal Scottish Museum, Edinburgh, that only the fishergirls could definitely be attributed to Scotland.

It has been suggested that a tartan pattern on a figure is evidence of its Scottish origin, but actually the tartan was almost equally popular in England, especially, after 1847, when the Prince of Wales, shortly before his sixth birthday, donned

[1] The author does not state whether these bear a maker's mark, nor on what evidence they are known to have been made in Scotland.

Highland dress on his first visit to Scotland. This delighted the public, and there-after he wore it on such great state occasions as the Opening of the Great Exhibition in 1851, the royal visit to Paris in 1855, and the wedding of the Princess Royal in 1858. Meanwhile the popularity of the dress had been even increased by the exploits of the Highland regiments in the Crimean War.

Interest in Scotland was also fostered by the great popularity of the works of Burns and Scott. Two figures of Burns are known by their marks to have been made by Sampson Smith, and there is no reason to suppose that most of the other figures of him and Scott and of characters from their works were not also made in England. A mould of 'Tam o' Shanter and Souter Johnnie' found among Sampson Smith's shows that even such a very Scottish poem had a vogue in England.

WALES

Many Victorian figures in excellent Staffordshire styles must have been primarily intended for Welsh markets. Among them are Carnarvon and Beaumaris Castles, and St Winefride, the patron saint of Holy Well in Flintshire; untitled figures of Welsh women in high-crowned broad-brimmed hats and of Welsh men in similar hats with lower crowns; and others with such titles as 'Welch Hunters', 'Welch Goat' and 'Welsh Shepherds'. All these would be pleasant souvenirs for the English visitors who flocked to Wales every summer, but there are at least two, the portraits of Christmas Evans (*Pl.* 40), chief minister of the Baptist churches in Anglesey, and John Elias (*Pl.* 39), Calvinistic Methodist preacher in Anglesey and Carnarvonshire, which could interest few but the Welsh. This has suggested that they, and perhaps all these Welsh figures, were made in a Welsh pottery; and the suggestion is fortified by the use on some figures of the spelling 'Welch', which was then obsolete in England except in the titles of the Welch Regiment and the Royal Welch Fusiliers. If there was a Welsh factory, it is likely to have been in North Wales, since Evans, Elias, St Winefride and the Castles are all connected with the north; and a figure entitled 'Langolen 1 Mile' and a portrait of Edward Morgan (*Pl.* 52), the Llangollen ploughman, further suggest that it was in that neighbourhood. But neither the present Llangollen Pottery nor Miss Dorothy Hartley, of Llangollen, can find evidence of any pottery there or elsewhere in North Wales which made such figures. At that period, Miss Hartley states, there was much traffic between Staffordshire and North Wales, and to this day gypsies follow old pack-horse routes from Stafford with pottery which they sell in the local markets. Dr Peate, Curator of the Welsh Folk Museum, Cardiff, has always understood that these figures were made in Staffordshire. He considers that the portraits of Evans and Elias were in such demand among the Welsh that it paid the Staffordshire potters to make them.

A NOTE ON MAKER'S MARKS

Only three portrait figures have been recorded with makers' marks; the Burns with Highland Mary (118g) with 'S. Smith / Longton / 1851', the Burns (118f) with 'Sampson Smith / Longton Staff / 1882', and the Lord Roberts (86a) with 'Hanley / Lancasters Limited / England'.

'S. Smith / Longton / 1851' has also been found on a dog, and on a pair of musicians. 'S. Smith / Longton / England' is on a pair titled '6 a.m.' and '6 p.m.', and 'Sampson Smith / 1851 / Longton'[1] on a number of dogs, and also on a 'Tam o' Shanter & Souter Johnny' illustrated in *Country Life* (10 Feb. 1955), but exactly the same figure has been found with the mark 'Sampson Smith / Longton Staff / England 1892'.

From the styles of the pieces marked 1851 it is clear that they were made much later; presumably the date records Sampson Smith's move to Upper High Street. The other dates, 1882 and 1892, each found on only one figure, may be the real date of the manufacture of that piece or of its original model.

The only other mark noted is 'Unwin' on a figure of two harvesters, but it cannot be definitely assigned to any one of the five Unwin firms working in Longton or Hanley between 1859 and 1925.

'Copyright / Dec 20 1901 / I. H. Sandland' is found in indented caps. on some specimens of the post-Victorian figures, King Edward VII (5p) and Queen Alexandra (68).

[1] This mark was also used for a few years on new pieces made from the old moulds discovered in 1948.

CHAPTER FOUR

Markets and Prices

MARKETS

It has proved impossible to secure any definite information about the marketing of Staffordshire figures in the Victorian era. The firms which made them appear to have preserved no records, and enquiries published in Staffordshire newspapers have elicited no informative answers. There can be no doubt however that the figures were sold in markets, fairs, and shops in most districts of Great Britain. Sir Herbert Read's statement that 'the pottery figure was never meant to be more than a cheerful ornament in a farmhouse or a labourer's cottage' can hardly be correct. It is true that until recently very many farmhouses and cottages had at least one figure on a mantelpiece, but there are many figures, especially those of theatrical characters, which must have been intended for a more sophisticated and urban public.

From the figures themselves it is clear that the manufacturers were not intent on a purely local trade; with the possible exception of a few preachers no portraits are found of local worthies unknown to the rest of England.

In some neighbourhoods the figures seem to be exceptionally numerous, and a quarter of a century ago, when I remarked on the large number in Swanage, an old man told me that some fifty years earlier, before the railway reached Swanage, there was considerable sea traffic of the local stone to Staffordshire, and that the ships brought hundreds of these figures in their return cargoes.

Though many portrait figures were made of Americans, they seem to have been intended primarily for the home market. In his article 'Staffordshire Figures in America' (*Connoisseur*, Nov. 1935) Mr Albert Lee states that few, even of those which might appeal to Americans on patriotic grounds, were exported there before the 1870's. 'The majority', he says, 'of the figures which are now included in public and private American collections are not there because of the initiative of the Staffordshire potters and their sales agents, but because the American traveller and the American collector went to England, and were captivated by the charm and quality of these products. It was not until the mid-Victorian era, and after the close of the Civil War, that Americans began to visit Europe in large numbers.' By 1935, when Mr Lee wrote, many thousands of the figures had already crossed the Atlantic; 'they possess', he considered, 'a certain virility, and even individuality, which are recognised to-day, perhaps more so in America than in England. Possibly for that reason it will be in America that the most complete and most characteristic products of the Victorian figure-makers will be found. Examples of almost all the pieces representing American subjects have been gathered into American museums.'[1]

PRICES

Many years ago I was told of an antique dealer who had some old price-lists of Staffordshire figures, but, before I could get to him, he had destroyed them as worthless. No contemporary list has yet been found, but a Catalogue issued by William Kent in the early years of the present century gives the then current wholesale prices per dozen of many nineteenth-century figures of which Kent's still had moulds. As the prices of most industrial products remained fairly constant from 1850 to 1910, if there was no great change in the processes of their manufacture, it may be surmised that Kent's prices in this list do not differ much from those of the original makers. The list includes the following portrait figures which will be found in my Catalogue, more than half of them derived from the 'Tallis' factory.

(a) 'Tallis' figures		Per dozen		Per dozen
Falstaff (129a)	$9\frac{1}{2}''$	11/–	$6\frac{3}{4}''$	7/6
Hamlet (126b)	$10\frac{3}{4}''$	12/–	$6\frac{3}{4}''$	7/6
Shylock (127b)	$9\frac{3}{4}''$	11/–	$7''$	7/6
Macbeth (127c)	—	—	$8\frac{1}{4}''$	8/6
Lady Macbeth (135a)	—	—	$8''$	8/6
Romeo & Juliet (133a)	$10\frac{1}{2}''$	18/–		
Lord Dundreary (136a)	$8\frac{1}{2}''$	8/6		
Garibaldi on horse (69h)	$15''$	36/–		
Victor Emmanuel on horse (41d)	$15''$	36/–		
Wellington on horse (20a)	$11\frac{1}{2}''$	24/–		
Prince on horse (5h)	$7\frac{3}{4}''$	11/–		
Princess on horse (6a)	$7\frac{3}{4}''$	11/–		

[1] There are portraits of Washington, Franklin, Lincoln, John Brown, the Cushman sisters, Hackett, Mrs Bloomer, Van Amburgh, Rarey, Heenan, Moody and Sankey, and many figures of the characters in *Uncle Tom's Cabin*. Mr Lee mentions a portrait of Mrs Beecher Stowe, but I have never seen it or any illustration of it.

		Per dozen		Per dozen
Garibaldi and horse (69g)	14"	60/–	8¾"	20/–
Napier and horse (71a)	8½"	20/–		
Garibaldi at War (69e)	—	—	9¼"	9/6
Gordon (80a)	16"	20/–		

Note. The last columns concern figures of which the larger versions appear in the Catalogue.

(b) Other figures

		Per dozen
Wellington	5"	2/6
Queen box (1k)	7¼"	8/6
Gladstone (28c)	11½"	10/–
Beaconsfield (26b)	11½"	10/–
Wolseley on horse (79c)	15"	22/–
Macdonald on horse (84b)	15"	22/–
French on horse (87b)	15"	22/–
Roberts (86b)	14"	14/6
Kitchener (83d)	14"	14/6
King Edward VII (5n)	14"	18/–
Queen Alexandra (6f)	14"	18/–

Since the above are wholesale prices, the retail prices were probably at least 50 per cent higher. The simple 5″ Wellington, 2½d. to the retailer, may have been 4d. to the public, and the 5/- Garibaldi and horse, the heaviest and most complicated of these portrait figures, not less than 8/-.[1]

It is clear from these Tables that the 'Tallis' factory figures, being more elaborate, were considerably more expensive; its 15″ equestrian figures cost 36s. a dozen whereas the others cost 22s. It is probable that Table (b) is the better guide to the prices of figures in the broader style, produced from only one or two moulds, such as were made by Sampson Smith.

[1] Kent's Price List for 1939, of which Messrs Mander & Mitchenson have a copy, shows the prices about 4½ times as big. The King Edward VII, for instance, had risen from 18s. to 80s. per dozen.

CHAPTER FIVE

The Designers

No record has been found of the designers of these figures. The manager of a pottery has generally an assistant who does any casual designing required, and it is probable that all, or nearly all, these Victorian portraits were designed by such assistants. To this day many of the figures turned out by the potteries are designed by artisans. I was shown round one establishment by the man who both designed its models and made the master-moulds. Nowadays such a man will have had some training in an art school, and his work has not the individuality and charm of un-sophisticated folk art.

Except for some figures of the early forties the designers generally made a real attempt to represent the features and clothes of the persons they purported to portray. The likenesses may be crude, but it is seldom in doubt whether an untitled piece represents Peel or Wellington, Albert or Napoleon III. Bernini required three Van Dyck portraits of Charles I and Henrietta Maria before he would attempt their busts, but these designers had the almost impossible task of making their three-dimensional models from one drawing or engraving. It is unlikely that any-one ever sat to them; photographs were hardly available before the sixties; and they must have had to rely on such engravings as they could obtain. One of the dangers of dependence on such sources is illustrated by the full-length figure of the Pope (*Pl.* 41). The engraving must have been only half-length, or the designer would not have ended his soutane above his knees and finished him with trousers.

So far the sources of very few models have been identified. Messrs Mander & Mitchenson have shown that the seven Shakespearean figures were based on en-gravings in Tallis' *Shakespeare Gallery*, and Mrs Joyce has discovered the originals of Pilch and Box (*Pl.* 52), Burns (118d), Peel (*Pl.* 13), Kossuth (*Pl.* 12), and Turkey England France (*Pl.* 18) by laborious research through the *Illustrated London News*. The Prince of Wales (*Pl.* 11) comes from Winterhalter's portrait, Captain Cook (*Pl.* 46) from Nathaniel Dance's, and Jemmy Wood (*Pl.* 48) from the woodcut in his *Life and Anecdotes*.

[4.] General Booth 110a

CHAPTER SIX

Processes of Manufacture

PRESS-MOULDS

Nearly all Victorian Staffordshire portrait figures were moulded in press-moulds made of plaster-of-Paris. The designer made a solid model of the figure, including its plinth, slightly larger than the intended figures, so as to allow for their shrinkage during their drying and firing. From this model a master-mould was made or, if the model was complicated, a number of master-moulds. Any one mould cannot conveniently be made in more than two or three pieces, and any one piece of it can only cover so much of a mould as has not more than one re-entrant angle in it; if there are more than one it is impossible to detach the piece. In such a case the model must be dissected, and each part of it moulded separately,[1] but the production of figures or parts of figures from moulds involved many separate operations, and some of the best potters soon learnt to economise by having their figures designed for reproduction by a single two-piece mould.

When it was desired to produce any considerable number of figures all the following operations were required:

(1) The designer made his model, generally of an oily clay (A).

(2) The model (A) was encased in a mould of two or three pieces (B), made, as were all further moulds, of plaster-of-Paris.

(3) This mould (B), the master-mould or 'case', was removed in pieces from the model (A). The model had generally been damaged in this moulding and was of no further use.

(4) The pieces of the master-mould (B) were put together again, and the hollow was filled with liquid plaster-of-Paris (C).

(5) When the plaster had set, the pieces of the master-mould (B) were again detached, leaving the Block (C), a solid replica of the original model.

The Block was carefully stored for use if the master-mould ever got damaged.

---

[1] Formerly the subsidiary parts had been made by hand, but by the Victorian period all but the smallest were made in moulds. To avoid the expense of many moulds re-entrants were sometimes made by hand when the figure was still soft after its first emergence from the mould.

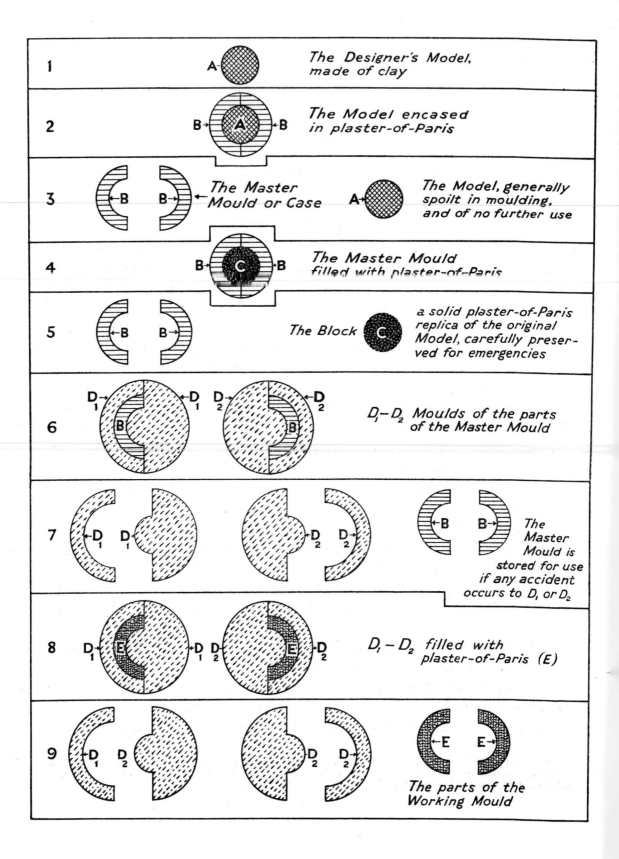

1	The Designer's Model, made of clay	
2	The Model encased in plaster-of-Paris	
3	The Master Mould or Case	The Model, generally spoilt in moulding, and of no further use
4	The Master Mould filled with plaster-of-Paris	
5	The Block — a solid plaster-of-Paris replica of the original Model, carefully preserved for emergencies	
6	D_1–D_2 Moulds of the parts of the Master Mould	
7	The Master Mould is stored for use if any accident occurs to D_1 or D_2	
8	D_1–D_2 filled with plaster-of-Paris (E)	
9	The parts of the Working Mould	

(6) The pieces of the master-mould (B) were each separately encased in moulds (D1 and D2).

(7) The pieces of the moulds (D1 and D2) were detached, and the master-mould (B) was stored for use if D1 and D2 suffered any damage.

(8) D1 and D2 were put together again, and their hollows filled with liquid plaster-of-Paris (E).

(9) When the plaster had set, the pieces of D1 and D2 were detached, leaving two plaster objects (E) similar in all respects to the pieces of the master-mould (B). These objects became the first working-mould.

From a working-mould up to 200 figures could be pressed without serious deterioration, but, by repeating operations (8) and (9), a number of working-moulds were made (even if only 200 figures were required) in order to avoid delay. Not more than two figures, or three in summer, could be made from one mould in a working-day because it needed time to dry after each usage.[1]

(10) A bat (flat sheet) of damp 'body' (clay mixed with some finely ground ingredients), of the thickness required for the intended hollow figure, was laid upon each piece of the working-mould, and pressed well into it with a sponge or other implement, the surplus at the edges being trimmed off with a knife.

(11) The pieces of the mould, after the trimmed edges had been painted with slip (clay diluted to the consistency of cream), were fitted together, and, after some hard pressure, tied tightly with string.

(12) Through the bottom of the mould, which was still open, thin rolls of clay were pressed into the seams by fingers or some implement to join together the pieces of the figure.

(13) The mould, being of porous plaster, absorbed the moisture from the clay, and the clay, as it dried, shrank and became detached from the plaster, and soon became firm enough (leather- or green-hard) to be handled. The pieces of the mould were then removed, and the figure could be stood on any flat surface without sagging.

(14) The open bottom of the figure was then closed by pressing into it a one-piece mould of the same size as the opening, and with its convex side covered with a bat of 'body'.[2] As the 'body' dried, the mould was detached, leaving the figure with a slightly domed bottom.

---

[1] If very few figures were required they could be made from the master-mould, and operations (6) to (9) would be avoided.

[2] A few early royal models were produced both in porcelain and earthenware, and some of the porcelain figures were left with open bottoms. Copies of a large pressed-earthenware portrait of Sir Walter Scott, untitled, have been found with open bottoms, but I have seen none except the cheap little figures of Sister Hallahan and Père Moulaert.

(15) While the figure was still fairly soft, the Repairer (also known as the Sticker) scraped away (fettled) the marks of the mould's seams, and corrected any faults, such as cracks or depressions caused by bubbles in the clay, by dabbing on some slip and filling them with clay.

(16) The Repairer stuck on, with a little slip, any parts made from subsidiary moulds, and any 'roughing' required to represent objects which have a surface too rough for moulding. Grass, for instance, could be reproduced by pressing clay through a sieve and applying the shreds to the figure with a knife, while less rough surfaces, such as sheep's wool, could be obtained by painting parts of a figure with slip and sprinkling it with granulated clay.

The Repairer also cut any small interstices in the figure which were too small to be conveniently made in the moulding, such as the gap below a horse's head and above the reins as they stretch from the bit to the neck. And he made a little hole, generally in the bottom of the figure, to enable the air to escape when the figure was fired, and saved it from being blown to pieces, but this is not really necessary if a figure is properly fired.

(17) After further drying the figure was fired in the first and hottest oven at about 1100° C., whence it emerged as 'biscuit', so called because it was as brittle as biscuits although it had not been twice cooked.

(18) Any underglaze colour required was then painted on the 'biscuit' with sugar or flour or fat oil, and hardened-on by firing at 600° to 700° C. Glaze was expensive and difficult to make and keep pure; without this hardening-on the colours were liable to come off when dipped in the glaze, and so tint the glaze and discolour all the figures dipped in it. This firing was not needed if the colour had been painted with gum arabic, but the gum was very expensive, and probably used seldom on these figures.

(19) Since 'biscuit' is porous, the figure was dipped into a liquid lead-glaze, and then fired in the 'glost' oven at about 950° C. There the glaze, partly composed of silica, was transformed into a film of glass enveloping the whole figure.

Great care was taken to employ a glaze which in cooling contracted uniformly with the 'body' of the figure. If the glaze shrinks more, little cracks (crazing) will appear in it sooner or later; if less, it will flake off (scale) at the edges. Fine crazing is found on nearly all genuine nineteenth-century figures, but not on most modern reproductions.

(20) The figure was then painted with its enamel (overglaze) colours, including gold. Enamel colours are metallic oxides mixed with a flux which vitrifies at comparatively low temperatures. So the figure was fired at from 750° to 850° C. in the

kiln. At these temperatures the glaze might soften again and fuse with the flux of the enamels.

With its emergence from the kiln the figure was complete.

It should be noted that no two complete figures can be exactly similar in all respects, even if they were pressed in the same working-mould. Besides the very gradual blunting of the mould in each successive usage, there are inevitably some slight variations in the handiwork even of the most skilled Repairer, especially in sticking on any subsidiary parts, which, being then still rather soft, may get altered in shape and stuck on at slightly different angles. There must also be some differences in the colouring, even if none is intended.

It should be noted that sharp figures may not be earlier than blunt ones, since they may have come from a new set of working-moulds made by the potter from the master-mould when his former set had become worn.

SLIP-MOULDS

Very few portrait figures were cast from slip-moulds. I have records of only four, the bust of Havelock (63f), dating from 1857, and the crude figures of Mr and Mrs Gladstone (28f and 29a) and the imposing bust of General Booth, dating from the 1890's.

The working slip-mould was made by the same operations (1) to (9) above as the working press-mould. At that point the bare pieces of the slip-mould were tied together, and slip was poured in through the opening until the mould was full. The plaster then absorbed the water from the nearest slip and after not more than half an hour a layer of clay of the required thickness had formed against the mould, and the rest of the slip was poured away. When the layer had dried to leather-hardness, the pieces of the mould were detached.

Figures cast from one mould, e.g. the four portrait figures mentioned above, were left with open bottoms. Cast figures with closed bottoms were made from two or more parts, each cast separately with an open end, and these ends were stuck together so that no opening remained.

To complete the figure all the same operations, (15) to (20), were required as for pressed figures.

The chief disadvantage of casting is that the working mould is very quickly deteriorated by the water in the slip, and cannot be at all satisfactorily employed for more than twenty figures. A very large number of working moulds are required for any popular model.

CHAPTER SEVEN

The Colouring

All colour on these figures is either underglaze or enamel; no instances of coloured glaze have been found.

UNDERGLAZE

Colours seen through the glaze acquire depth and brilliance, and under its protection they are stable and permanent. Unluckily nearly all the inexpensive paints could not stand the heat of the glost-oven; only cobalt blue and a black made of cobalt mixed with manganese and iron could be employed.

Cobalt oxide, the foundation of all blue paints employed on ceramics, is unalterable by any heat however intense. Its extraction from cobalt ore was an expensive process, but its colour is very strong, and about 1802 Thénard, a French chemist, invented a compound, 30 parts cobalt to 100 parts alumina, which greatly reduced the expense without sacrificing much of the richness of the colour. By 1840, when even a poor quality of cobalt oxide cost 6s. per lb. in England, Thénard's blue was available at 1s. 3d. and at about this date it began to appear on Staffordshire figures.[1] For the next twenty years it was very freely used, giving the figures the sparkling appearance which is one of their chief attractions. Then for some unascertained reason, perhaps merely a change in the public's taste, the blue almost ceased to be used. With the exception of the bust of General Booth (*Pl.* 4), which cannot date from earlier than the 1890's, no dateable figure later than the Prince of Wales with Princess (*Pl.* 10) of 1863 has been found with undeniably underglaze blue. There are however blue passages on some copies of the Pope, Cardinal Manning, and O'Connell (*Pl.* 41), three of the monumental figures made by Sampson Smith in the later seventies, but the blues are less rich and may be

[1] Dr Glaisher's diary, in a note on the Napoleon III (*Pl.* 19) which he bought in 1913, wrote of 'the bright blue which appears in Staffordshire figures in about the period 1840–1860'. It occurs however on a number of excellent untitled figures some of which have been identified by Messrs Mander and Mitchenson with figures found in theatrical prints of the 1820's and 1830's. They have however all the Victorian characteristics except that they have open bottoms, and Messrs Mander and Mitchenson are inclined to agree with me that they differ so much in colour and material from figures known to be pre-Victorian that they were probably made after 1837. Some of them are found both in porcelain and in earthenware, but all appear to have come from the same pottery.

enamels. It is not always easy to distinguish underglaze colour from enamel. One method, often recommended but not quite conclusive, is to scratch the surface with a sharp implement; it will make a mark on enamel but, if used with force, will also make a mark on glaze. Underglaze can sometimes be detected by the colour having spread beyond its bounds in the glost oven; the overlap, being under the glaze, cannot be removed.

Underglaze black, though much more effective than enamel black, which generally has a dull matt surface and is liable to flake off, was rarely used, because it needed exceptional skill to make a compound of cobalt, manganese, and iron which did not show a brown or bluish tinge, especially where it was thinly painted. It is found on Jemmy Wood (153a), which dates from the early forties, and on the four preachers, Christmas Evans (*Pl.* 40), Elias, O'Bryan and Raffles (*Pl.* 39), all probably of that decade. In the fifties it was used on the hats and boots of some Crimean figures, Napoleon III (*Pl.* 19), Admirals Napier and Dundas (*Pl.* 21), Generals Brown and Simpson (*Pl.* 23), and on the coat of the young Spurgeon (*Pl.* 43). Its most lavish use, probably, in that decade, was on the figures of Dick Turpin (150a and b), in which not only his hat, boots, and hair, but also his mare, Black Bess, are in underglaze black. In the sixties Frank Gardiner (*Pl.* 52), made from the same model as Turpin (150a), was similarly painted. Sampson Smith still possess the master-mould of Turpin (150b), and it is probable that they also made (150a), which is very similar in design. In the seventies the same firm used underglaze black freely on their monumental figures of O'Connell (*Pl.* 41), and Gladstone, Beaconsfield, Moody and Sankey (*Pl.* 42). Thereafter only enamel black seems to have been used; the few undateable figures with underglaze black (e.g. Penn (*Pl.* 47), St Vincent de Paul (*Pl.* 40), Wesley (97b) and Spurgeon (*Pl.* 43) all probably date from before the seventies.

ENAMELS

Enamel colours are metallic oxides mixed with a vitreous flux which are painted on the glaze or printed on it by transfers or by metal or rubber stamps. Pale enamels, those in which the colouring matter is small in proportion to the flux, often, after their firing in the kiln, have a glazed appearance, but deeper colours, in which the proportion of flux is less, generally have a duller surface, and are liable to flake off, especially if exposed to the soaping and rubbing of a good housewife. Such blemishes are often repainted but, unless the figure has been refired, the new paint can be easily removed with acetone.

Throughout our period gold overglaze painting was much used for titling, and also for incidental decoration, in the early years on top of the prevalent underglaze blue passages, and later on the extensive white areas found on nearly all figures. Gold was seldom painted over other enamel colours, because it would necessitate a second firing in the kiln. For many years the painters used 'best gold' (also called 'mercuric gold'), an amalgam of gold and mercury with flux, which, after being fired in the kiln, was so dull that it had to be burnished with agate stone or, more economically but less effectively, rubbed with a special sand; it was also very liable to be rubbed off, especially where it had been applied to small protuberances such as the 'raised capital' lettering. Early in the eighties Messrs Johnson, Matthey & Co. introduced a liquid preparation, 'Bright Gold', which issued from the kiln with a bright surface, saved the expense of burnishing, and was more stable. Since then it has been employed on popular earthenware, but it has a deeper and harsher colour than 'best gold', and the latter is still employed on more expensive pottery.

Three portrait figures, Bazaine (*Pl.* 37), Orton (*Pl.* 50), and I. O. G. T. (*Pl.* 8), are sometimes found with no paint on them; their body is yellowish, with some brown stains on it; their glaze is uncommonly thin, and there are blue specks in it; and they much resemble salt-glaze ware. But whereas salt-glaze is thicker above than beneath any projections, and is very thin on the bottoms, in these figures the glaze is thickest on the bottoms, as it normally is on figures which have been dipped head downwards into lead-glaze. There are highly coloured lead-glaze figures made from the same moulds of Orton and I. O. G. T., and it is unlikely that a factory produced the same figure both in salt-glaze and lead-glaze.

It is probable (1) that the body of these figures acquired its yellow tinge by being fired at excessive heat in the biscuit-oven, and that the brown stains were caused by the iron, which was generally present in the clay, getting burnt; (2) that the figures were then dipped in a lead-glaze in which some cobalt had been dissolved in order to correct the yellow tinge and, being insufficiently ground, caused the blue specks when fired in the glost-oven; (3) that the thinness of the glaze was due to the abnormal hardness of the biscuit when it was dipped; and (4) that the figures were thought too defective to be worth painting, but might be saleable at low prices.

There are also two figures, smaller versions, 10″, of Moltke and Bismarck (*Pl.* 37), which have uncoloured faces and hands, but enamel black on their boots and swords, and on their horses' eyes, manes, and tails, and brown on their bridles and reins. Both have good bluish glaze, no yellow tinge, and very little brown stain; neither has been found with more coloured parts. It seems probable that they were designed to be issued in this state.

CHAPTER EIGHT

Introduction to the Catalogue

The entries in this Catalogue are generally limited to Victorian figures which were intended to be portraits of contemporary or historical persons, and do not include imaginary representations of characters from books or plays, nor of historical characters of whose features there is no record. I have however admitted a number of non-portrait figures, e.g. the Crimean fortresses, which help to illustrate the extent of the public's interest in contemporary events.

So many figures were made in the 1840's of the Queen and Prince Albert, and of the royal children with or without their parents, many of them having little merit, that it has seemed inadvisable to catalogue more than a selection from them. I have also omitted some of the many smaller figures of Wellington, Nelson, and Napoleon I which have no fundamental difference in design from those included in the Catalogue.

In the final, 'Historical', section of the Catalogue most of the figures were possibly, but improbably, based on authentic portraits. It is probable that many of them were based on scenes from the contemporary theatre, but not necessarily as portraits of the actual actors.

COLOURING

Colours have not been noted, because they vary on equally authentic contemporary pieces from the same model. The Wellington (20j), for instance, is found with his coat blue, black, red, or white.

SIZE

The height given for each figure is that of the tallest example within my knowledge. Many of the more popular figures were originally made in more than one size, generally with some slight alterations in their designs; Moody and Sankey (*Pl.* 42) are found $17\frac{1}{2}''$, $13\frac{1}{2}''$, $11\frac{1}{2}''$, and $9''$ high. In Plate 1 Albert and Napoleon III in its largest size, $12\frac{1}{2}''$, is shown with its midget, $4\frac{1}{2}''$.

There are also slighter differences in height. Where two figures differ in height alone, the base of one of them has been truncated, but where they differ in all their

41

proportions, the smaller figure may come from a mould which was made not from the 'block' but from an existing figure, and so have incurred a second shrinkage of from one-eighth to one-fifth.

DATE

A definite date has been entered against a figure only where there is a strong presumption that the model was made in relation to some event, but, even so, it may not be quite exact. For instance the models of the Prince of Wales (5 i–m) and the Princess Alexandra (6 a–e) were almost certainly made after the official announcement of their engagement on the 1st of November 1862 and before their wedding on the 10th of March 1863, since all but one of the Prince are titled 'Prince of Wales', while those of the Princess are all titled 'Princess' and none of them 'Princess of Wales'. For all of them I have given 1862, though some may have been made in 1863. Similarly the Crimean personages are dated with the year in which they were first prominent in the war.

Individual figures made from these models cannot, of course, be dated; some are being made even a hundred years later. There are however some criteria of a figure's age; if it has underglaze blue on it, it is probably not much later than 1863; if it has 'bright gold', it is not earlier than 1880; if it shows no crazing, it is generally of recent manufacture, but some undoubtedly early figures are found uncrazed.

There are some models which can be approximately dated although they cannot be proved to be connected with any specific event. Because the monumental Queen Victoria (*Pl.* 15) is often found with inscriptions commemorating the Jubilees of 1887 and 1897, and is generally in company with the bearded Prince of Wales (*Pl.* 15), it might be thought that both these models belong to that late period. But this Queen Victoria is also found, generally much more firmly modelled, with no inscription but 'Queen of England'. In this state it closely resembles the Queen of Prussia (*Pl.* 35) in the details of its modelling, in its sparse and pale colouring, and in its gilt titling and decoration. The figure of the Prince, too, is almost identical with the Duke of Edinburgh (*Pl.* 15) which, with its pair, the Grand Duchess Marie (*Pl.* 15) in her Russian tiara and bridal veil, must date from between the announcement of their engagement in May 1873 and their marriage in January 1874. The pose of the Prince and Duke is identical with the King of Prussia's (*Pl.* 35).

The King and Queen of Prussia cannot date from later than January 1871 when they became Emperor and Empress of Germany, and are unlikely to be earlier than

July 1870, when the Franco-Prussian War began, and for a few months the German cause was very popular in England.

All these six monumental figures clearly came from the same factory, and four of them certainly date from 1870 to 1874. It is likely therefore that the Queen Victoria and the Prince also date from the early seventies. They may have been made to commemorate the Thanksgiving Service in St Paul's Cathedral in February 1872 for the Prince's recovery from typhoid, when the Queen, very reluctantly, emerged from her long seclusion.

Another problem is the dating of the anti-Catholic figures, Cranmer, Ridley and Latimer, Popery, Protestantism, and '£10,000' (Pl. 38). All five have a somewhat pre-Victorian appearance, and the inscription on Popery of a pronouncement made by the Archbishop of Dublin in 1816 also suggests that they belong to the period of the agitation against Catholic emancipation. But they have all the 'Tallis' characteristics, and this same pre-Victorian style is found in the 'Tallis' factory's Winter's Tale and Romeo and Juliet (Pl. 16), which cannot be earlier than 1852.[1] A peculiarity in the painting of Perdita's dress in Winter's Tale, that the recesses of its folds show touches of pink paint while the projections are left white, is also found in the painting of the girls' skirts in Protestantism and '£10,000', and fortifies the suggestion that they belong to the same period. 1851 was the year of the violent No Popery agitation aroused by the Pope's giving English territorial titles to bishops. For its first three months *Punch* abounded in scurrilous anti-Catholic propaganda, and in March published a cartoon, 'The Kidnapper', of a monk holding out a veil to a girl who carries a bundle labelled 'L.s.d.', which is exactly the theme of '£10,000'. In these circumstances it has not seemed rash to presume that these models were made in 1851.

LETTERING

Many portrait figures, including most of the royal figures of the forties, bear no titles. Most of them can be identified by their resemblance to titled figures, e.g. the recent discovery of Dr Raffles (Pl. 39) led to the identification of a smaller version, which I had wrongly thought to be of a Church of England clergyman because he wore surplice, gown, and bands. Others, e.g. Lord Shaftesbury (Pl. 7), Dr Goulburn (Pl. 51), Captain Webb (Pl. 48), and L. E. Landon (Pl. 32), can be identified with much probability; in such cases the evidence is given in the Catalogue. A few figures which are probably portraits have defied identification, and have had to be omitted.

[1] See Ch. III.

INTRODUCTION TO THE CATALOGUE

The following varieties of lettering have been found:

(1) *Raised caps.* These capital letters may be made in three ways, (i) by being designed on the original model, and so reproduced in the mould; (ii) by being 'sprigged', i.e. impressed on each figure before its first firing from a separate mould; (iii) by being impressed by a roller on which the letters have been engraved in reverse. It is generally impossible to distinguish the process, but the first, being more economical of labour, is likely to have been generally used.

Raised caps. were generally gilt, but on many figures the gilt is now so worn as to be hardly perceptible. From 1854 onwards they were sometimes enamelled black.

(2) *Indented caps.* These were stamped on each figure separately before its first firing. On some figures the indentations are very shallow because the body had become too dry before it was stamped. From 1847 they were much used by the 'Alpha' factory; in the fifties the 'Tallis' factory used them on most of their Shakespearean figures, and was still using them in 1864 on Garibaldi at Home (*Pl.* 33). They are found on no figures which can be definitely dated later than 1864.

Indented caps. were generally painted gold or black, but on some figures appear to have been left uncoloured.

(3) *Gilt script.* Hand-painted upper and lower case letters were much used throughout the Victorian era. The earliest dateable examples are Sir R. Sale and Lady Sale (*Pl.* 32) of 1842, but Van Amburgh (*Pl.* 48) may be even earlier.

(4) *Hand-painted gilt caps.* The only certain example is Jemmy Wood (*Pl.* 48), which cannot be later than 1844, but in some figures made from worn moulds it is difficult to decide whether there are vestiges of moulded lettering under the gold.

Painted gilt caps. are found on some modern reproductions of models which originally had indented caps.

(5) *Hand-painted black caps.* Only found on some of the later 'Tallis' figures, e.g. Lord Napier (*Pl.* 47) of 1867.

(6) *Transfers.* Printing from transfers, or perhaps from metal or rubber stamps, was much used by the 'Tallis' factory, both in titles, in caps., and in inscriptions, in upper and lower case, as on Ridley & Latimer, Popery (*Pl.* 38), and some of its Shakespearean figures. They are generally printed black, but the inscriptions are sometimes in gold. On Gordon (*Pl.* 50), the factory's latest model, the title is crimson transfer. There is no record of transfer titles on figures from any other factory. On late copies of some 'Tallis' figures the black titles appear to be hand-painted.

Except for raised caps. which were part of the original model all these processes were employed after the figure had been moulded; raised caps made by separate

44

moulds or rollers, and indented caps. before its first firing, and all the others after its emergence from the glost oven. It is therefore possible, though probably un-common, that even figures from the same working mould were given different sorts of titling, or that some were titled and others left untitled. The titling there-fore provides no definite evidence that one copy was made earlier or later than another, but where a figure is found both titled and untitled I have entered the titled copy, and where one is found with various methods of titling I have entered 'raised caps.', 'indented caps.', and 'transfers' rather than 'gilt script' and the other hand-painted methods.

A few figures have been found with two different titles, *viz.*, 'Dick Turpin' (150b) and 'Frank Gardiner' (*Pl.* 52), 'Wallace' (191b) and 'Bruce' (192a), and a smaller version of 39g with 'Eugenie & Napoleon' (which is clearly correct) and 'Queen & Albert'. The same figure without change of title was used for the Prin-cess Royal (*Pl.* 9) and, four years later, for the Princess of Wales (6c). The same design was used, but perhaps not in the same sizes, for Washington and Franklin.

CHAPTER NINE

The Catalogue

(1) THE ROYAL FAMILY

1. QUEEN VICTORIA (1819–1901)
*Queen 1837–1901. Married Prince Albert
~~Feb. 1840~~*

a QUEEN (indented caps.) 7″ 1838–9 **Pl. 7**
Sitting, crowned. Book in right hand.

b NO TITLE 5″ n.d.
Standing, crowned. Orb in right hand, sceptre
in left.

c NO TITLE 6¼″ 1840 **Pl. 5**
Sitting, crowned.
Pair to 2a (P. Albert).

d NO TITLE 8¼″ 1840 **Pl. 6**
Standing, crowned. Open book on pedestal to
her right.
Pair to 2b (P. Albert).

e NO TITLE 12″ 184– **Pl. 5**
Standing, crowned. Both hands on book to
her left.
Pair to 2c (P. Albert).

f NO TITLE 13½″ 184–
Standing, crowned, in short cloak. Right hand
holds a flower in front of her waist.

g NO TITLE 11¾″ 184–
Almost same design as (f), but no flower.
Pair to 2d (P. Albert).

h QUEEN VICTORIA (gilt script) 11″ 184–
Standing, crowned. Left hand on waist, right
holding reticule.
Pair to 2e (P. Albert).

i VICTORIA (raised caps.) 9½″
Standing, crowned. Orb in right hand.

j NO TITLE 9″ **Pl. 12**
Standing, crowned, beside a lion.

k NO TITLE 7¼″
In two pieces ('Queen's Box' in Wm. Kent's
Lists). Standing, crowned. Hands clasped on
her skirt.

l NO TITLE 7″ 184–
On horse facing left. Crowned
Pair to of (P. Albert).

m QUEEN (raised caps.) 9″ 184– **Pl. 8**
On horse facing left. Low round hat, with
plume and scarf. Left hand holds reins in her
lap.
Pair to 2g (P. Albert).

n NO TITLE 8″ 184–
On horse facing left. High round hat with
scarf. Both hands in her lap.
Pair to 2h (P. Albert).

o QUEEN OF ENGLAND (gilt script) **Pl. 15**
17½″ 187–
Standing, crowned.

p QUEEN OF ENGLAND & EMPRESS OF INDIA.
CROWNED JUNE 20TH 1837. YEAR OF JUBILEE
1887 (gilt script) 16¾″ 1887
Copy of (o).

q QUEEN OF ENGLAND & EMPRESS OF INDIA.
CROWNED JUNE 20TH 1837. YEAR OF JUBILEE
1897 (gilt script) 16″ 1897
Another copy of (o).

WITH PRINCE ALBERT AND A CHILD

r PR. ALBERT & QUEEN (raised caps.) **Pl. 22**
12½″ 184–
All standing. *Left*, Albert in Highland dress;
Centre, Queen, bare-headed; *Right*, child in
plumed bonnet.

s NO TITLE 8¼″ 184– **Pl. 6**
Left, the Queen sitting, a baby in long clothes
in her lap; *Right*, Albert standing, his right
arm round her shoulders.

WITH THE PRINCESS ROYAL

t NO TITLE 5½″ 1841 **Pl. 5**

Sitting. The Princess in long clothes in her lap.
> Pair to 2j (P. Albert).

u NO TITLE 7″ 1841   **Pl. 5**
Standing, crowned. Princess on her right arm.
> Pair to 2k (P. Albert).

v NO TITLE 7″ *c.* 1843   **Pl. 6**
Sitting, crowned. Right arm on Princess's shoulder.
> Pair to 2r (P. Albert).

w NO TITLE 9¾″ *c.* 1843
Standing, crowned. On her right Princess standing on a goat.
> Pair to 2s (P. Albert).

WITH THE PRINCE OF WALES

x NO TITLE 8½″ 1842   **Pl. 6**
Sitting, wearing a very large double-arched crown. In her lap the Prince, in a short frock, and three-feathered hat. A lion and a unicorn beside her feet.
> Pair to 2l (P. Albert).
> *Note.* In a smaller version, 7″, the Prince is omitted.

WITH NAPOLEON III

y QUEEN EMPEROR (raised caps.)   **Pl. 20**
11″ 1854
Standing, crowned, with the Emperor on her left.

WITH THE KING OF SARDINIA

z QUEEN & KING OF SARDINIA (raised caps.)
14″ 1854   **Pl. 19**
Standing, crowned. The King on her left, with a dog between his legs.

aa NO TITLE 9″ 1854
Queen standing on the right of a clock, King on the left; their hands clasped over it.

WITH NAPOLEON III AND THE KING OF SARDINIA

bb THE ALLIED POWERS (raised caps.) **Pl. 18**
12″ 1854
The Queen, crowned, standing, with Napoleon on her right and the King on her left, both in cocked hats.

WITH NAPOLEON III AND THE SULTAN

cc TURKEY. ENGLAND. FRANCE. (raised caps.)
10¼″ 1854   **Pl. 18**

The Queen standing, crowned, with the Sultan in a turban on her right, and the Emperor bare-headed on her left.
> From a medal by A. A. Caque struck at the Paris Mint in 1854, and reproduced in the *Ill. Lon. News* of September 9th.

2. PRINCE ALBERT OF SAXE-COBURG-GOTHA (1819–61)

Feb. 1840, m. Queen Victoria. 1857, created Prince Consort
See also 1r, s (Queen Victoria)

a NO TITLE 6½″ 1840   **Pl. 5**
Sitting, bare-headed. Paper in right hand.
> Pair to 1c (Victoria).

b NO TITLE 9″ 1840   **Pl. 6**
Standing, crowned. Left elbow on a pedestal.
> Pair to 1d (Victoria).

c NO TITLE 12″ 184–   **Pl. 5**
Standing, bare-headed, in Garter robes.
> Pair to 1e (Victoria).

d ALBERT (raised caps.) 11½″ 184–
Standing, bare-headed, in uniform with trousers, and long cloak. Left hand holds his sword.
> Pair to 1g (Victoria).

e PRINCE ALBERT (gilt script) 11″ 184–
Standing, bare-headed, dressed as (d); cloak draped over a pedestal.
> Pair to 1h (Victoria).

f NO TITLE 8¼″ 184–
On horse facing right. Cocked hat, knee boots.
> Pair to 1l (Victoria).

g ALBERT (raised caps.) 9½″ 184– **Pl. 8**
On horse facing right. Cocked hat, uniform and trousers.
> Pair to 1m (Victoria).

h NO TITLE 8″ 184–
On horse facing right. Cocked hat, swallow-tailed coat and trousers.
> Pair to 1n (Victoria).

i ALBERT (raised caps.) 7½″ 1854
On horse facing right. Cocked hat and knee boots.
> Pair to 42b (Sultan).

j NO TITLE 5½″ 1840   **Pl. 5**
Sitting, bare-headed, in military frock-coat.
> Pair to 1t (Victoria).

k NO TITLE 7½″ 1840   **Pl. 5**
Standing, bare-headed, in long cloak, uniform
with trousers.
  Pair to 1u (Victoria).

l NO TITLE 8½″ 1842   **Pl. 6**
Sitting, bare-headed, in uniform and trousers.
Lion and unicorn beside his feet.
  Pair to 1x (Victoria).

m NO TITLE 11½″   **Pl. 36**
Standing, bare-headed, in swallow-tailed coat.

n NO TITLE 11″   **Pl. 20**
Standing, bare-headed, in uniform and
trousers.

o NO TITLE 13½″   **Pl. 36**
Standing, bare-headed, in uniform and
trousers.

p ROYAL STAG HUNT (gilt script) 10″
Below, two hounds chasing a stag uphill to the
right; *Above*, Albert galloping to the right in
top hat and long coat.

WITH THE PRINCESS ROYAL

q NO TITLE 9½″ *c.* 1844
Standing, in cocked hat with high plume. His
right hand holding the Princess's left. She in
tricorn hat, short skirts and socks.

WITH THE PRINCE OF WALES

r NO TITLE 7½″ *c.* 1843   **Pl. 6**
Sitting, bare-headed. His left arm on the
Prince's shoulders.
  Pair to 1v (Victoria).

s NO TITLE 10¾″ *c.* 1843
Standing, in cocked hat. His left arm round
the waist of the Prince, who stands on a goat.
  Pair to 1w (Victoria).

WITH NAPOLEON III

t NAPOLEON ALBERT (raised caps.) 13¼″ 1854
Both standing in cocked hats, a wall and a
heap of shells between them. *Left*, Napoleon
under the Union Jack; *Right*, Albert under
the Tricolor.

u NO TITLE 12½″ 1854   **Pl. 1**
Similar design to (t), but *left*, Napoleon in a
kepi under the Tricolor, and *right* Albert in a
cocked hat under the Union Jack.

v NAPOLEON PRINCE ALBERT (gilt script) 14½″
1854   Same design as 2t.

3. PRINCESS ROYAL (1840–1901)
Victoria, eldest daughter of Queen Victoria. In

1858 *m. Prince Frederick William of Prussia.
Mother of Kaiser William II.*
  See also 1t–w (*Victoria*), *and* 2q (*Albert*)

a NO TITLE 5″ 1842
Sitting, bare-headed, in high-backed chair
surmounted by a crown. Wears short skirt and
socks.
  Pair to 5a (P. of Wales).

b PRINCESS (indented caps.) 6¼″ 1846 **Pl. 7**
Standing by a round table with her hand on a
parrot.
  Pair to 5b (P. of Wales).

c PRINCESS (raised caps.) 13¾″ 1857   **Pl. 9**
On horse facing left, with plumed hat and veil.
  Pair to 4a (P. Fk. Wm.).
  Note. This model was also used for the
Princess of Wales (6c).

WITH PRINCE OF WALES

d PRINCE AND PRINCESS (indented caps.)
7½″ 1844
Standing in a pony carriage, with the Prince
astride the pony.

e NO TITLE 9¼″ 1844   **Pl. 8**
Both asleep on a sofa, with crowns above their
heads; an angel standing behind.

WITH PRINCE FREDERICK WILLIAM

f PRINCESS ROYAL & FRᴷ OF PRUSSIA (raised
caps.) 16″ 1857   **Pl. 10**
Standing, bare-headed. The Prince on the left.

4. PRINCE FREDERICK WILLIAM OF PRUSSIA (1831–88)
Son of King William I of Prussia. In 1858 *m. the
Princess Royal. In* 1861 *became Crown Prince, and
in March* 1888 *German Emperor, but died a hun-
dred days later.*
  See also 3f (*Pss Royal*)

a PRINCE FRᴷ Wᴹ (raised caps.)   **Pl. 9**
14¼″ 1857
On horse facing right. In cocked hat, saluting.
  Pair to 3c (Pss Royal).

b PRINCE F. PRUSSIA (raised caps.) 10½″ 1857
Almost same design as (a), but with a cloak
over his uniform, and his right hand not
saluting but on his thigh.

c CROWN PRINCE (gilt script) 10″ 1870
On horse facing left. In plumed helmet, knee
boots, and heavy beard.

5. PRINCE OF WALES (1841–1910)

Albert Edward, eldest son of Queen Victoria. In March 1863 m. Princess Alexandra of Denmark. In 1901 succeeded as King Edward VII.

See also 1x (Victoria), 2r and s (Prince Albert) and 3d and e (Pss. Royal)

a   NO TITLE   5″   1842
Sitting, bare-headed, in high-backed chair surmounted by a crown.
    Pair to 3a (Pss Royal).

b   PRINCE (indented caps.)   6¼″   1846   **Pl. 7**
Standing, bare-headed, by a round table, a ship in his left hand.
    Pair to 3b (Pss Royal).

c   NO TITLE   12″   *c*. 1848   **Pl. 11**
Standing, in a sailor suit.
    From Winterhalter's portrait (1847) now in Buckingham Palace.
    Note. Ill. Lon. News for 14 Oct. 1848 shows a similar figure in Parian ware made by Minton with P. Albert's consent.

d   PRINCE OF WALES (raised caps.)   **Pl. 11**
15″   *c*. 1852
Standing, in Highland dress, with a dog.

e   P OF WALES (raised caps.)   9¼″   1859 **Pl. 12**
Standing, bare-headed, in military tunic and trousers.
    Pair to 7a (P. Alfred).
    Note. He and P. Alfred received their first commissions in 1859.

f   PR OF WALES (raised caps.)   11″   1859
Standing bare-headed, beside a broad chair, in tunic and trousers.
    Pair to 7b (P. Alfred).

g   PRINCE OF WALES (raised caps.)   **Pl. 11**
14″   1862?
Standing bare-headed, in civilian dress, with a dog.

h   PRINCE OF WALES (indented caps.)   **Pl. 38**
7¾″   1862
On horse facing left. Bare-headed, in civilian clothes.
    Pair to 6a (Pss of Wales).

i   PRINCE OF / WALES (raised caps.)   **Pl. 13**
11¾″   1862
On horse facing right. In high bonnet, plaid and kilt.
    Pair to 6b (Pss of Wales).

j   PRINCE OF WALES (raised caps.)   13″   1862
On horse facing right. Bare-headed, in civilian dress. His right hand on a plumed hat.
    Pair to 6c (Pss of Wales).

k   PRINCE OF WALES (raised caps.)   10″   1862
On horse facing right. Bare-headed, in civilian dress. His right hand on a top-hat.
    Pair to 6d (Pss of Wales).

l   PRINCE (raised caps.)   9½″   1862
Standing, bare-headed, in civilian dress. Top-hat in left hand.
    Pair to 6e (Pss of Wales).

m   PRINCE OF WALES (gilt script)   **Pl. 15**
18″   187–
Standing, bearded and bare-headed, in uniform with trousers.

n   KING EDWARD VII (indented caps.)   14″   1902
Standing, bearded, in cocked hat; Garter cloak over uniform with trousers. Speech in left hand.
    Pair to 6f (Pss of Wales).

o   KING EDWARD (raised caps.)   13″   1902
Standing, nearly bald, in uniform. Cocked hat in his right hand.
    Pair to 6g (Pss of Wales).

p   KING EDWARD VII (raised caps.)   13¼″   1901
On horse facing right. In cocked hat, uniform, and knee boots.

WITH THE PRINCESS OF WALES

q   PRINCE & PRINCESS (raised caps.)   15¾″   1862
Standing. *Right*, the Prince in civilian dress, top-hat in left hand; *Left*, the Princess, her hair in a snood, and hat over her right arm.

r   PRINCE & PRINCESS (raised caps.)   9½″   1862
Same design as (r), but no snood.

s   NO TITLE   14¼″   1862   **Pl. 10**
Standing. *Left*, the Prince in civilian dress, top-hat in right hand; *Right*, the Princess, bare-headed, hat over left arm.

6. PRINCESS OF WALES (1844–1925)

See also 5 q, r, and s

a   THE PRINCESS (indented caps.)   **Pl. 38**
7¾″   1862
On horse facing right. Bare-headed.
    Pair to 5h (P. of Wales).

b   PRINCESS (raised caps.)   10¾″   1862 **Pl. 13**
On horse facing left. In plumed bonnet.
    Pair to 5i (P. of Wales).

c   PRINCESS (raised caps.)   13¼″   1862
On horse facing left. In plumed hat with veil.
    Pair to 5j (P. of Wales).
    Note. The same model as 3c (Pss Royal).

d PRINCESS (raised caps.) 9½″ 1862
On horse facing left. In flat hat with plume and veil.
    Pair to 5k (P. of Wales).

e PRINCESS (raised caps.) 9½″ 1862
Standing, wearing a snood, hat on her right arm.
    Pair to 5l (P. of Wales).

f QUEEN ALEXANDRA (indented caps.)
14″ 1902
Standing, in small crown, long veil, and cloak.

    Pair to 5n (P. of Wales).

g QUEEN ALEXANDRA (raised caps.) 13″ 1902
Standing, in low crown.
    Pair to 5o (P. of Wales).

h QUEEN OF ENGLAND (transfer script)
15″ 1902
Standing, in crown and veil, long dress, and ermine cloak.

7. PRINCE ALFRED (1844–1900)

Second son of Queen Victoria. In 1866 created Duke of Edinburgh. In 1874 married the Grand Duchess Marie Alexandrovna of Russia.

a P ALFRED (raised caps.) 8¼″ 1859
Standing, bare-headed, in naval costume. Right arm on a capstan, left hand holding a hat.
    Pair to 5e (P. of Wales).

b PR. ALFRED (raised caps.) 10½″ 1859
Standing beside a broad chair, bare-headed, in naval costume.
    Pair to 5f (P. of Wales).

c PRINCE ALFRED (raised caps.) **Pl. 12**
10¾″ 1859
Standing, bare-headed, in naval costume. Right hand on a capstan, left holding a hat. A coil of rope near his left foot.

d DUKE OF EDINBURGH (gilt script) **Pl. 15**
17″ 1874
Standing, bearded and bare-headed, in uniform with trousers.
    Pair to 8a (Dss of Edinburgh).

8. DUCHESS OF EDINBURGH
(1853–1920)

a DUCHESS OF EDINBURGH (gilt script) **Pl. 15**
17″ 1874

Standing, in bridal veil and Russian tiara.
    Pair to 7d (D. of Edinburgh).

9. DUKE OF CONNAUGHT (1850–1942)

Arthur, third son of Queen Victoria. In 1882 commanded the Guards Brigade in Wolseley's Egyptian campaign.

a DUKE / OF CONNAUGHT (raised caps.)
14″ 1882
On horse facing left. In helmet, uniform, and knee boots.
    Pair to 79a (Wolseley).

b DᴱCONNAUGHT (raised caps.) 11¾″ 1900
On horse facing right. In helmet.
    Same series as S. African War (General,
83c etc.

10. PRINCESS ALICE (1843–78)

Second daughter of Queen Victoria. In 1862 m. Prince Louis of Hesse (later Grand Duke of Hesse-Darmstadt).

a Pˢ ALICE (raised caps.) 8¼″ 1862 **Pl. 52**
On horse facing left. In pill-box hat.
    Pair to 11a (P. Louis of Hesse).

11. PRINCE LOUIS OF HESSE
(1837–92)

a P L OF HESSE (raised caps.) **Pl. 52**
9½″ 1862
On horse facing right. Bare-headed, in civilian dress.
    Pair to 10a (Pss Alice).

12. PRINCESS LOUISE (1848–1939)

Fourth daughter of Queen Victoria. In 1871 m. the Marquess of Lorne, who in 1900 succeeded to the Dukedom of Argyll.

a PRINCESS LOUISE (raised caps) **Pl. 5**
12¾″ 1871
Standing, in hat and flounced skirt.
    Pair to 13a (M. of Lorne).

13. MARQUESS OF LORNE (1845–1914)

a MARQUESS OF LORNE (raised caps.) **Pl. 5**
12¾″ 1871
Standing, in Highland dress.
    Pair to 12a (Pss Louise).

14. ADOLPHUS, DUKE OF CAMBRIDGE (1774–1850)

Seventh son of George III, and uncle of Queen Victoria, and grandfather of Queen Mary. In 1818 m. Princess Augusta of Hesse-Cassel.

a DUKE / OF CAMBRIDGE (raised caps.) **Pl. 9**
  14½″ 184–
  On horse facing left. Bare-headed, in uniform.
    Pair to 15a (Dss of Cambridge).

b DUKE / OF CAMBRIDGE (raised caps.) **Pl. 9**
  9″ 184–
  On horse facing right.
    Nearly same design as (a) reversed.
    Pair to 15b (Dss of Cambridge).

15. AUGUSTA, DUCHESS OF CAMBRIDGE (1797–1889)

a DUCHESS (raised caps.) 14½″ 184– **Pl. 9**
  On horse facing right.
    Pair to 14a (D. of Cambridge).

b DUCHESS (raised caps.) 9″ 184–
  On horse facing left.
    Nearly same design as (a).
    Pair to 14b (D. of Cambridge).

16. GEORGE, DUKE OF CAMBRIDGE (1819–1904)

Only son of Adolphus. In 1840 married morganatically Louisa Fairbrother who took the name Mrs FitzGeorge. Commanded a Division in the Crimea. Commander-in-Chief 1856 to 1895.

a DUKE / CAMBRIDGE (raised caps.) **Pl. 23**
  8″ 1854
  On horse facing right.
    Same series as smaller versions of Crimean Generals, 45b etc.

17. LEOPOLD, KING OF THE BELGIANS (1790–1865)

Uncle of Queen Victoria. In 1816 m. Princess Charlotte, only child of George IV; she died the next year. In 1831 chosen to be the first King of the Belgians.

a LEOPOLD KING OF BELGIUM (gilt script)
  9″ 184– **Pl. 20**
  Standing, bare-headed, in uniform.

18. DUKE OF CLARENCE (1864–92)

Eldest son of Edward VII. Betrothed to Princess Mary (May) of Teck in 1891, but died before the wedding.

a DUKE OF CLARENCE (raised caps.) **Pl. 50**
  15½″ 1891
  Standing, bare-headed, in uniform.
    Pair to 19a (Pss May).

19. PRINCESS MAY (QUEEN MARY) (1867–1953)

a PRINCESS MAY (raised caps.) **Pl. 50**
  15¾″ 1891
  Standing, bare-headed.
    Pair to 18a (D. of Clarence).

(2) STATESMEN

20. DUKE OF WELLINGTON
(1769–1852)

1841–6, in Peel's Cabinet, but without office;
1842–52, Commander-in-Chief

a UP GUARDS AND AT THEM (Upper and lower case, transfer) 11½″ **Pl. 16**
On horse facing right. In uniform. Telescope in right hand.

b NO TITLE 9¼″
On horse facing right. In cocked hat, uniform, and cloak. Right hand, holding his baton, on the saddle-cloth.

c WELLINGTON (raised caps.) 16¾″
On horse facing right. In cocked hat and uniform. Baton in his right hand. The plinth, 5½″ high, decorated with grapes and vine leaves.
  Pair to 34a (Napoleon I).
  Note. Sampson Smith's have the moulds of both figures, but no contemporary copies have been found.

d NO TITLE 7″
On horse facing right. In cocked hat, uniform, and a cloak fastened round his neck. Right hand on his hat.
  Pair to 34c (Napoleon I).

e NO TITLE 7¾″
Standing, in cocked hat, tailed coat, and knee-boots, in front of a square pedestal.

f NO TITLE 9″
Standing, in cocked hat and long coat with epaulets.

g WELLINGTON (gilt script) 10″ **Pl. 12**
Standing, bare-headed, in uniform with trousers. Left fore-arm resting on a cannon.

h WELLINGTON (gilt script) 18″
Standing, facing half-right, bare-headed, in frock-coat. Right hand on hip, left holding a speech.

i WELLINGTON (raised caps.) 16″ **Pl. 2**
Same design as (h).

WELLINGTON (gilt script) 13″
Standing, same design as (h), except the right hand grasps the edge of his coat, and left rests on a draped pedestal.

k NO TITLE 10″
Standing, bare-headed, in civilian dress, with a cloak held together by both hands at his waist. A pedestal against his left leg.
  Pair to 33e (Nelson)

l WELLINGTON (gilt script) 12″ 185– **Pl. 31**
Sitting in a high-backed armchair, bare-headed, with crossed knees

m WELLINGTON (raised caps.) 11½″ 185–
Same design as (l) except that head leans to the left, right hand holds a book, and there are openings in the back of the chair.

n NO TITLE 6½″
Sitting in a high-backed armless chair, facing to his left. Left hand on the seat behind him, right holds a speech.

o NO TITLE 13½″ 1852 **Pl. 33**
Standing, bare-headed, in military dress. On a square two-tiered base, inscribed at the back TO THE / MEMORY OF THE / DUKE OF / WELLINGTON (indented caps.).

21. DANIEL O'CONNELL (1775–1847)

Irish patriot; agitated for Catholic Emancipation and Home Rule. Elected M.P. in 1829, and was Lord Mayor of Dublin in 1841. Convicted of sedition, but acquitted on appeal, in 1844.

a D O CONNELL (raised caps.) 16″ **Pl. 2**
Standing, bare-headed. Right hand on hip, left on a draped pedestal. Low-crowned hat on a draped pedestal beside his right leg.

b DAN O'CONNELL (gilt script) **Pl. 41**
17¾″ 187–
Standing, bare-headed. Right hand on hip, left on a draped pedestal.

22. SIR ROBERT PEEL (1788–1850)

Prime Minister 1834–5 and 1841–6. In 1846 repealed the Corn Laws

a PEEL (small raised caps.) 16½″ **Pl. 51**
Standing, bare-headed. Right hand, holding speech, on his waistcoat, left on hip.

b SIR / R / PEEL (gilt script) 10″ **Pl. 36**
Standing, bare-headed. Right hand holding
speech against his leg, left on hip. The title on
pedestal behind his right leg.

c S. R. PEEL (indented caps.) 7½″ **Pl. 7**
Standing, bare-headed. Right hand, holding
speech, in front of his waist, left grasping the
edge of his coat. Low wall behind him.

d NO TITLE 9¾″ **Pl. 46**
Standing, bare-headed. Right hand holding
speech near his hip, left touching a closed
book on a pedestal.

e SIR R PEEL (gilt script) 8¼″ c. 1846
Standing, bare-headed. Left-hand on hip,
right on top of a pedestal with a scroll inscribed in gilt script 'Repeal of the Corn Law'.

f SIR R PEEL (gilt script) 10″ 1850 **Pl. 13**
On horse with docked tail facing left. In top-
hat and civilian dress, a cloak over his right
shoulder.
  Same design as an engraving in Ill. Lon.
News of 6 July 1850.

23. THOMAS SLINGSBY DUNCOMBE
(1796–1861)

M.P., 'the best-dressed man in the House'. In
1840 supported the Chartists, and in 1848 presented
the People's Petition, signed by over three millions,
to the House of Commons.

a T S DUNCOMBE (gilt script) **Pl. 47**
9″ c. 1848
Standing, bare-headed, in frock-coat. His
right hand on a paper inscribed 'Presedent of
the Trades' in gilt script.

24. EARL OF SHAFTESBURY
(1801–85)

Philanthropist. In 1848 advocated the Ragged
Schools, and the reclamation of juvenile offenders

a NO TITLE 7½″ c. 1848 **Pl. 7**
Sitting, bare-headed, a small boy standing
between his knees.
  Note. In shape of head, hair style, and
clothes, closely resembles the painting of
Shaftesbury by Sir Francis Grant in the King
Edward Institute & Good Shepherd Mission
(Photo. in Nat. Portrait Gall.).

b NO TITLE 7½″ c. 1848 **Pl. 48**
Standing, bare-headed. Left hand on the head
of a small boy.

25. LOUIS KOSSUTH (1802–94)

Hungarian patriot. In 1848 led the revolt against
Austria, and fled to Turkey in 1849. In 1851 came
to England, and was received with great popular
demonstrations.

a NO TITLE 11″ 1851
Standing in high, flat-brimmed hat with
plume. Left hand on his waist, right on a
draped pedestal.
  Note. Same design as engraving in Ill. Lon.
News, 15 Nov. 1851.

b KOSSUTH (gilt script) 10¾″ 1851 **Pl. 36**
As (a) but low, flat-brimmed hat, and right
hand on a cloak draped over a wall.

c KOSSUTH (gilt script) 10½″ 1851 **Pl. 12**
As (b), but hat has curled brim.

26. EARL OF BEACONSFIELD
(1804–81)

Benjamin Disraeli, created Earl in 1876. Prime
Minister 1868 and 1874–80. Author of Coningsby,
Lothair, etc.

a BEACONSFIELD (gilt script) **Pl. 42**
16½″ 187–
Standing. Left hand on pedestal.
  Pair to 28b (Gladstone).

b BEACONSFIELD (raised caps.) 12″ 187–
As (a).
  Pair to 28c (Gladstone).

27. RICHARD COBDEN (1804–65)

M.P. 1841–65. He and John Bright were the
principal agitators for the repeal of the Corn Laws

a R. COBDEN (indented caps.) **Pl. 7**
7½″ c. 1846
Sitting, a cornucopia against his right leg.

b R COBDEN (gilt script) 8½″ c. 1846
Standing, bare-headed. Right hand on his
hip, left holding a paper against his leg; a
pedestal behind it.

28. WILLIAM EWART GLADSTONE
(1809–98)

Prime Minister 1868–74, 1880–5, 1886, 1892–4

a NO TITLE 12″ **Pl. 39**
Standing, bare-headed. On square base. Right
hand on two books on a square pedestal.

b GLADSTONE (gilt script) 16″ 187– **Pl. 42**
Standing, bare-headed. Right hand on speech
on pedestal.
> Pair to 26a (Beaconsfield).

c GLADSTONE (raised caps.) 12″ 187–
As (b)
> Pair to 26b (Beaconsfield).

d W. E. GLADSTONE (raised caps.) 12½″
Standing, bare-headed. Axe in right hand.
Large flag, with Union Jack in one corner,
above his left shoulder.

e GLADSTONE (gilt script) 15¼″
Standing, bare-headed. Left hand, holding a
speech, on a tree trunk.

f MR GLADSTONE (raised caps.) 10¾″ 189–
Standing, bare-headed. Left hand on a
pedestal, right holding a speech against his
waistcoat. A cast figure.
> Pair to 29a (Mrs Gladstone).

29. MRS GLADSTONE (1813–1900)

Catherine, daughter of Sir Stephen Glynne, Bart.
Married Gladstone in 1839

a MRS GLADSTONE (raised caps.) 10½″ 189–
Standing, wearing a cap, and holding a fan in
her left hand. A cast figure.
> Pair to 28f (Gladstone).

30. CHARLES STEWART PARNELL
(1846–91)

*Leader of the Irish Parliamentary Party from
1874 to 1890. In 1886 converted Gladstone to
Home Rule.*

a C. S. PARNELL (raised caps.) **Pl. 17**
13¾″ 188–
Standing, bare-headed, in Greek dress with
bare arms and legs. A heavy club in his left
hand; his right holding up a flag with the
Union Jack and Irish Harp embossed on it.
> Apparently adapted from some figure of
> Hercules holding up the Nemean Lion.

b NO TITLE 15¼″ 188– **Pl. 51**
Standing, bare-headed. The beard and clothes
(low turned-down collar, knotted tie, square-
cut coat with broad lapels) agree with portraits of Parnell in *Ill. Lon. News*, vol. 77
(1880), p. 493, and vol. 88 (1888), p. 383.

(3) NAVAL AND MILITARY

1. PRE-VICTORIAN PERSONS

31. ADMIRAL BLAKE (1599–1657)
Commander of the British Fleet in the Dutch War (1652–3)

a ADMIRAL BLAKE (gilt script) 10½″ **Pl. 43**
Standing, bare-headed, in short coat, breeches, and stockings.

32. CAPTAIN JAMES COOK (1728–79)
The circumnavigator

a NO TITLE 7½″ **Pl. 46**
Sitting beside a round-topped table.
From the portrait (1766) by Nathaniel Dance in the Painted Hall at Greenwich.

33. LORD NELSON (1758–1805)

a DEATH OF NELSON (gilt script) 8¼″ **Pl. 22**
In cocked hat, worn athwartships, seated on the ground. *Right*, an officer kneeling, bare-headed, right hand on Nelson's shoulder, left holding Nelson's left hand; *Left*, a civilian, bare-headed, holding a mug towards Nelson. The ends of two lanyards, with rings, overhang the base.

b DEATH OF NELSON (gilt script) 8″
As (a) except that Nelson is raised on a seat beside the civilian, there is a chairback behind the officer, and there are no lanyards.

c DEATH OF NELSON (gilt script) 8¾″ **Pl. 22**
Sitting, bare-headed, supported on each side by an officer, both standing in cocked hats worn fore and aft.

d DEATH OF NELSON (gilt script) 8¼″
Sitting, bare-headed. *Right*, an officer standing; *Left*, an officer sitting. Both officers in cocked hats.

e NO TITLE 10½″
Standing, in cocked hat (athwartships), an anchor behind his right leg.
Pair to 20k (Wellington).

f NO TITLE 8½″
Standing, dressed as in (a). Left forearm on a gun emplacement.

g NO TITLE 6″
Standing, dressed as in (a). A fluted pedestal against his left leg.

34. NAPOLEON I (1769–1821)

a NAPOLEON (raised caps.) 16¼″
On horse facing left. In cocked hat, short overcoat, and knee boots. On a high plinth, 5½″, decorated with grapes and vine leaves.
Pair to 20c (Wellington).

b NO TITLE 9½″
On horse facing left. In cocked hat, long coat, and a cloak over his right shoulder, blowing out behind him.

c NO TITLE 7″
On horse rearing and facing left. In cocked hat, uniform, and knee-boots, his cloak blown out to his right. His right arm lifted against it.
Pair to 20d (Wellington).

d NO TITLE 8″
Sitting, bare-headed, on rocks, in uniform and stockings. His hat and sword beside his left leg; his left arm over a rock.
Note. Probably represents him at Elba or St Helena.

e NO TITLE 11¾″ **Pl. 22**
Standing, in cocked hat, uniform, overcoat, and knee-boots. Right hand inserted in waistcoat, left behind his back. An eagle by his left side.

f NO TITLE 7½″
Standing, in cocked hat, long-tailed uniform, and knee-boots. His arms folded on his chest; a draped pedestal beside his left leg.

g NO TITLE
Standing, facing half-left, in cocked hat, uni-

form, great coat, and knee-boots; the skirts of the coat blown out to his right.

    Note. Illustrated in *Connaissance des Arts* for May 1956, but its height not stated.

h NO TITLE 10¼″

Standing, bare-headed, in long-tailed uniform, breeches, and stockings. Right hand inserted in his waistcoat, left behind him.

2. AFGHAN WAR, 1842

35. SIR ROBERT SALE (1782–1845)

In command of the British retreat from Kabul, 1842

a SIR R SALE (gilt script) 8″ 1842 **Pl. 32**
On horse facing right. In cocked hat and uniform.
    Pair to 36a (Lady Sale).

36. LADY SALE (1790?–1853)

Florentia Winch, m. Sir Robert 1809. *Led the women in the retreat, and was taken captive. Published her* Journal *in* 1843.

a LADY SALE (gilt script) 7¼″ 1842 **Pl. 32**
On horse facing left. In high round hat and riding habit.
    Pair to 35a (Sir R. Sale).

3. ARCTIC EXPEDITION, 1845

37. SIR JOHN FRANKLIN (1786–1847)

Discoverer of the North-West Passage. Sailed with Erebus *and* Terror *in July* 1845. *From* 1847 *to* 1857 *thirty-nine expeditions were sent to find him. The last found evidence that he and all his men had perished in* 1847.

a SIR JOHN FRANKLIN (indented caps.) **Pl. 46**
10½″ 184–
Standing in naval uniform. Holding telescope in both hands.
    Pair to 38a (Lady Franklin).

38. LADY FRANKLIN (1792–1875)

Jane Griffin, m. Franklin 1828. *Between* 1850 *and* 1857 *fitted out five ships at her own expense to discover Franklin.*

a LADY FRANKLIN (indented caps.) **Pl. 46**
10½″ 184–
Standing, a wreath on her head.
    Pair to 37a (Franklin).

4. CRIMEAN WAR, 1854–56

39. NAPOLEON III (1808–73)

Nephew of Napoleon I; Proclaimed Emperor 1851. *England's ally in the war*
See also 1y, bb, cc (*Q. Victoria*), 2t u (*Albert*), *and* 66a (*Brit. Lion*)

a LOUIS NAPOLEON (raised caps.) **Pl. 19**
16″ 1854
Standing, bare-headed, in uniform. Cocked hat in right hand.

b NAPOLEON (raised caps.) 16″ 1854
Sitting, in cocked hat and uniform. Right arm on a cannon.

c EMPEROR OF FRANCE (raised caps.) **Pl. 20**
12¼″ 1856
Sitting, bare-headed, in uniform and cloak. A cocked hat on his right knee. Chair with high back surmounted by an eagle.
    Pair to 40c (Eugenie).

d EMPEROR (raised caps.) 8¼″ 1854
Sitting, bare-headed, in uniform, in an armchair with high perforated back. Cocked hat in right hand.
    Note. No. 382 in the Willett Collection (Brighton), but described as Francis II of Austria in the catalogue.

e LOUIS NAPOLEON (raised caps.) **Pl. 23**
12¾″ 1854
On horse facing right. In cocked hat and uniform. Left hand on the horse's head.
    Pair to 40a (Eugenie).

f LEWIS NEPOLIAN (raised caps.) 10″ 1854
(This extraordinary title is in the mould.)
On horse facing right. In cocked hat and
uniform.
    Also found with LOIS NAPOLEON (raised
caps.)

WITH THE EMPRESS EUGÉNIE

g EUGENIE & NAPOLEON (gilt script)   Pl. 51
12½″ 1854
Right, Napoleon standing, bare-headed, in
uniform; *Left*, the Empress sitting, a veil on
her head, in a broad-backed chair.
    Note. Also found wrongly inscribed QUEEN
& ALBERT (gilt script).

WITH THE EMPRESS EUGÉNIE AND THE PRINCE IMPERIAL

h NO TITLE 8″ 1856
Right, Napoleon standing, bare-headed, in
uniform; *Left*, Eugénie sitting, in two-
flounced skirt. Both arms holding the Prince
in her lap, with a shawl over both their heads.

40. EMPRESS EUGÉNIE (1826–1920)
Daughter of the Count of Montijo; m.
Napoleon in 1853
See also 39g h, (Napoleon III)

a EMPRESS OF FRANCE (raised caps.)   Pl. 23
11¼″ 1854
On horse facing left. In round hat with veil
hanging to her left.
    Pair to 39e (Napoleon III).

b EMPRESS (raised caps.) 10″ 1854
Almost the same as (a), except that veil hangs
to her right.

WITH THE PRINCE IMPERIAL (1856–79)

c EMPRESS OF FRANCE (raised caps.)   Pl. 20
12¼″ 1856
Sitting, a fillet round her hair, with both arms
holding the prince. Chair with highback surmounted by an eagle.
    Pair to 39c (Napoleon III).

d NO TITLE 8″ 1856
Sitting, crowned. The Prince in her lap, supported by her left arm, her right hand on his
chest.

41. KING OF SARDINIA (1820–78)
Victor Emmanuel II, ally in the war. State visit
to England in 1855, shortly after his wife's death.
Proclaimed King of Italy in 1861.
    See also 1z, aa, bb (Q. Victoria)

a KING OF / SARDINIA (raised caps.)   Pl. 21
17″ 1855
Standing, bare-headed. Right hand on a
draped pedestal.

b KING OF SARDINIA (raised caps.)   Pl. 19
15″ 1855
Standing, in cocked hat and uniform. Both
hands on his belt.

c K. OF SARDINIA (raised caps.) 11½″ 1855
On horse facing right. In cocked hat and uniform. Both hands on his lap.

d VICTOR EMMANUEL (transfer black caps.)
15″ c. 1864
On horse facing left.
    Pair to 69 (Garibaldi).
    Note. I have heard of a copy, but never seen
it. In Kent's earlier list it appears as a pair to
this Garibaldi.

42. THE SULTAN (1822–61)
Abdul Medjid, ally in the war
See also 1bb (Q. Victoria)

a THE / SULTAN (raised caps.)   Pl. 26
10¾″ 1854
On horse facing left. In plumed turban, long
coat, and Turkish trousers.
    Same series as 45b, 53a, and 56c.

b SULTAN (raised caps.) 7½″ 1854
On horse facing left. In round plumed hat,
short coat, and Turkish trousers.
    Pair to 2i (P. Albert).

43. ADMIRAL SIR JAMES DUNDAS
(1785–1862)
Commanded the Mediterranean Fleet 1853–4

a DUNDAS (raised caps.) 16″ 1854   Pl. 21
Standing, bare-headed, in naval uniform.
    Pair to 44a (Napier); also found 15″ as pair
to 44b (Napier).
    Pl. 21 illustrates the 15″ version.

44. ADMIRAL SIR CHARLES NAPIER
(1786–1860)
Commanded the Baltic Fleet 1854–5

a C. NAPIER (raised caps.) 16½″ 1854

Standing, bare-headed, in naval uniform. Hat in right hand, cloak in left.

Pair to 43a (Dundas).

b C. NAPIER (raised caps.) 15″ 1854 **Pl. 21**
Same design as (a), but a gun and shells against his right leg.

Pair to the 15″ version of 43a (Dundas).

c SIR CHARLES NAPIER (gilt script) **Pl. 27**
12¾″ 1854
Standing, bare-headed, in naval uniform. Telescope in right hand; left foot on a gun.

45. F-M. LORD RAGLAN (1788–1855)

Commanded British Army in the Crimea till his death in July 1855

a F M LORD RAGLAN (gilt script) **Pl. 19**
15½″ 1854
Standing, bare-headed, in military uniform.

b LORD / RAGLAN (raised caps.) **Pl. 26**
10½″ 1854
On horse facing left. In cocked hat and uniform.

Same series as 42a, 53a, and 56c.

46. GENERAL SIR GEORGE BROWN
(1790–1865)

Commanded the Light Division in the Crimea. Second-in-Command to Lord Raglan. 1855.

a G. BROWN (raised caps.) 13″ 1854
On horse facing right. Bare-headed. Holding a Scotch bonnet to his head with his right hand.

b G. BROWN (raised caps.) 13″ 1854 **Pl. 23**
On horse facing right. In cocked hat and uniform. Right hand holds a flag-staff, with the flag flying above his head.

Pair to 47a (Simpson).

c SIR / GEORGE BROWN (raised caps.) **Pl. 23**
8½″ 185–
On horse facing right. Bare-headed. Right hand holds cocked hat against the saddle.

Pair to 63e (Havelock).

47. GENERAL SIR JAMES SIMPSON
(1792–1868)

1854, Chief of Staff in the Crimea; 1855, succeeded Raglan as Commander of the British troops

a GNL. SIMPSON (raised caps.) **Pl. 23**
13½″ 1854
On horse facing left. In cocked hat and uni-

form. Left hand holds a flag-staff, with the flag flying above his head.

Pair to 46b (Brown).

b G SIMPSON (raised caps.) 17½″ 1854 **Pl. 24**
Standing, in cocked hat and uniform. Two flags, guns and shells against his right leg.

Same series as 48a (Windham), and 55a (Pelissier).

47A. GENERAL SIR GEORGE CATHCART (1794–1854)

Commanded the 4th Division in the Crimea until he was killed in a cavalry charge on 5 Nov. 1854.

a G CATHCART (raised caps.) 12½″ 1854
On horse facing right, in plumed cocked hat, swallow-tailed coat, and knee boots. Left fore-arm on a round object with smooth top, and tasselled sides.

48. GENERAL SIR CHARLES WINDHAM (1810–70)

Commanded the 4th Division in the Crimea

a G WINDHAM (raised caps.) **Pl. 24**
18″ 1854
Standing, in cocked hat and uniform. Sword, guns and shells against his right leg.

Same series as 47b (Simpson), and 55a (Pelissier).

49. GENERAL SIR WILLIAM CODRINGTON (1804–84)

1854, commanded Light Division in the Crimea. Nov. 1855, succeeded Simpson as Commander of the British troops.

a GNL CODRINGTON (gilt script)
11½″ 1854
On horse facing right. In round hat and uni-form. Left hand on the horse's head.

Pair to 55e (Pelissier).

b GNL CODRINGTON (raised caps.) **Pl. 27**
11½″ 1854
Standing, in round hat and uniform. Right hand on a flag; left leg against a gun.

50. COLONEL SIR GEORGE DE LACY EVANS (1787–1870)

1854, repulsed a sortie from Sebastopol

a SIR DE LACY / EVANS (raised caps.) **Pl. 27**
12½″ 1854

NAVAL AND MILITARY

Standing, bare-headed, in uniform. Cocked hat on table to his right; left hand on a pedestal.

51. GENERAL SIR WILLIAM FENWICK WILLIAMS (1800–83)
1855, defended Kars against the Russians

a SIR / W F WILLIAMS (raised caps.) **Pl. 23**
9″ 1855
On horse facing right. Bare-headed, in uniform.

52. FLORENCE NIGHTINGALE (1820–1910)

'The Lady with the Lamp'; reached Scutari with her nurses in Nov. 1854; returned to England in 1856.

a MISS / NIGHTINGALE (raised caps.) **Pl. 31**
14¼″ 1855
Standing, a veil on her head. Wears the locket, with a Cross on it, given by Queen Victoria.

b MISS / NIGHTINGALE (raised caps.) **Pl. 22**
9¾″ 1855
Standing, a veil on her head. To her right an officer sitting, bare-headed, left arm in a sling.

c MISS F / NIGHTINGALE (raised caps.) **Pl. 32**
10½″ 1855
Standing, bare-headed. A tray with two cups in her hand.

53. MARSHAL SAINT-ARNAUD (1801–54)

Commander-in-Chief of the French Army in the Crimea till his death in Sept. 1854

a MARSHAL / ARNAUD (raised caps.) **Pl. 26**
10″ 1854
On horse facing right. Bare-headed, in uniform. Right hand holding cocked hat on the horse's back.
Same series as 42a, 45b, and 56c.

54. GENERAL CANROBERT (1809–95)
Commander-in-Chief, in succession to Saint-Arnaud, from Oct. 1854 to May 1855

a CANROBERT (raised caps.) 11½″ 1854 **Pl. 27**
Standing, bare-headed, in uniform. His cocked hat in his left hand.

55. GENERAL PELISSIER (1794–1864)
Succeeded Canrobert as Commander-in Chief in May 1855

a G PELISSIER (raised caps.) 17½″ 1855 **Pl. 21**
Standing, in kepi and uniform. Two flags, guns and shells to his left.
Same series as 47b (Simpson) and 48a (Windham).

b GNL PELISSIER (raised caps.) 11½″ 1855
Standing, in cocked hat and military frock-coat. Left hand holds his sword against a heap of shells.

c GNL PELISSIER (raised caps.) 10″ 1855
Same design as (b), but the shells against his right leg.

d GNL PELISSIER (raised caps.) **Pl. 23**
12½″ 1855
On horse facing left. In cocked hat and uniform. The horse rearing, a gun beneath it.

e GNL PELISSIER (raised caps.) 12½″ 1855
On horse facing left. In cocked hat, tunic, cape, and trousers. Left arm on the horse's mane.
Pair to 49a (Codrington).

f GENERAL / PELISSIER (raised caps.) 9″ 1855
On horse facing left. Bare-headed. Cocked hat hanging from his left hand, the plume almost touching the ground.

56. OMAR PASHA (1806–71)
Commander-in-Chief of the Turkish forces throughout the war. Born a Croatian, he had deserted from the Austrian army in 1828, and turned Mahomedan.

a OMER PACHA (gilt script) 13″ 1854 **Pl. 25**
Standing, facing half-right, in fez, military frock-coat and trousers.

b OMAR PASHA (gilt script) 11″ 1854 **Pl. 27**
Standing, in fez, short tunic, and knee-boots.

c OMER / PACHA (raised caps.) **Pl. 26**
10½″ 1854
On horse facing right. In fez and frock-coat.
Same series as 42a, 45b, and 53a.

d OMER PACHA / SUCCESS TO TURKEY (type, upper and lower case) 10¾″ 1854 **Pl. 26**
On horse facing left. In fez and frock-coat.
Note. A 4½″ untitled version of this figure is still made by William Kent, Ltd, and listed as 'Emin Pasha on Horse'. They also make a pair to it with the horse facing left.

57. SEBASTOPOL

Russian fortress in the Crimea besieged by the Allies from Oct. 1854 until it fell in Sept. 1855

a SEBASTOPOL (raised caps.) 10¾″ 1854 **Pl. 28**
Gateway flank by two round towers; a French flag on the right tower. A Turkish soldier to the left of the gate, and an English soldier to the right.
  Note. The flag and the soldiers are from separate moulds. In some copies the positions of the soldiers are reversed, and/or the flag is on the left tower.

b SEBASTOPOL (raised caps.) 7½″ 1854
Same design as (a), but no soldiers.

58. MALAKOFF

An outwork of Sebastopol

a MALAKOFF (raised caps.) 7¾″ 1854 **Pl. 28**
A battlemented wall with a high central tower, and a smaller tower on the right. A French flag on either tower (see note to 57a).

59. THE REDAN

a THE REDAN (raised caps.) 8¾″ 1854 **Pl. 28**
A battlemented wall with a three-storied central tower. A French flag on the tower.

60. VICTORY (1856)

a THE VICTORY (raised caps.) 14¼″ 1856 **Pl. 30**
An English sailor sitting on a gun, a French soldier on his left, and a Turkish soldier on his right, both standing.

61. NON-PORTRAIT CRIMEAN FIGURES

From the innumerable excellent figures of sailors and soldiers these twelve have been selected for illustration.

a BRITAINS GLORY (raised caps.) 10½″ **Pl. 12**

b SCOTLANDS PRIDE (raised caps.) 10½″ **Pl. 12**

c NO TITLE (English sailor) 10″ **Pl. 12**

d NO TITLE (French soldier) 10″ **Pl. 12**
  Note. (c) and (d) are obverse and reverse of the same figure.

e THE WOUNDED / SOLDIER (raised caps.) 13″ **Pl. 18**

f THE / SOLDIERS FAREWELL (raised caps.) 13¼″ **Pl. 18**

g ENGLAND (raised caps.) 9½″ **Pl. 18**

h SCOTLAND (raised caps.) 10¼″ **Pl. 18**

i SOLDIER'S DREAM (raised caps.) 13¾″ **Pl. 29**

j NO TITLE (Soldier & Sailor) 13½ **Pl. 30**

k ENGLAND & FRANCE (raised caps.) 12″ **Pl. 32**

l READY WILLING (gilt script) 11¾″ **Pl. 36**
  Other capital figures are

m THE / SAILORS RETURN (raised caps.) 12½″
Sailor, holding his hat above his head, with his right arm round a girl.

n VIVANDIERE (raised caps.) 14″
A woman standing in front of a French soldier mounted on a horse facing right.

o BEGGING SAILOR (raised caps.) 16¼″
Also found with title SAILOR (raised caps.)
Standing, in straw hat, with a sailing boat on his left shoulder. His right hand on the bare head of a small boy, also in naval dress.
  Note. There is an untitled pair (16¾″) of a Highland soldier holding a flag flying behind his bonnet.

p NO TITLE 9″
Two Turkish soldiers in fezzes, one standing and the other sitting smoking in front of a domed mosque.

5. INDIAN MUTINY (1857–9)

62. GENERAL SIR COLIN CAMPBELL (1792–1863)

Commander-in-Chief in India 1857–60. Had previously commanded the 1st Division in the Crimea.

a SIR COLIN CAMPBELL (gilt script) **Pl. 12**
  10¾″ 1857

Standing, bare-headed, in short tunic and trousers. Left hand holding a round plumed hat to his head.

b SIR / COLIN CAMPBELL (raised caps.)
  11″ 1857

On horse facing right. In Scotch bonnet, long coat, and trousers.

Pair to 63c (Havelock).

c CAMPBELL (raised caps.) 9¾″ 1857
On horse facing right. In plumed bonnet, short tunic and trousers.

Pair to 63d (Havelock).

d SIR / C. CAMPBELL (raised caps.) **Pl. 13**
10¾″ 1857
On horse facing right. Bare-headed, in long coat and trousers. Bonnet in his right hand.

63. GENERAL SIR HENRY HAVELOCK
(1795–1857)

Recaptured Cawnpore July 1857, relieved Lucknow in September; in November, with Sir Colin Campbell, again relieved Lucknow, but died of dysentery the same day.

a MG . HAVELOCK . KCB (raised caps.) **Pl. 31**
13½″ 1857
Standing, bare-headed, in uniform.

b HAVELOCK (gilt script) 9¼″ 1857
Standing, bare-headed, in long military coat and trousers, left hand holding his sword.

c G HAVELOCK (raised caps.) **Pl. 13**
10¾″ 1857
On horse facing left. Wearing a hat with a sun-curtain.

Pair to 62b (Campbell).

d HAVELOCK (raised caps.) 8¾″ 1857
Same design as (c).

Pair to 62c (Campbell).

e SIR / H. HAVELOCK . CB (raised caps.) 9″ 1857
On horse facing left, bare-headed, in long coat and trousers. Left hand holding his hat on the horse's back.

Pair to 46c (Brown).

f LOCKNOW HAVELOCK CAWNPORE (raised caps.) 9″ 1857
Bust, bare-headed, in tunic. A cast figure.

64. HIGHLAND JESSIE (? dates)

Wife of Corporal Brown. On 26 Sept. 1857, when Lucknow was at its last gasp, in 'a wild unearthly scream' she shrieked that she could hear pipes playing 'The Campbells are coming', and inspired the garrison to hold out till they arrived.

a HIGHLAND JESSIE (raised caps.) **Pl. 29**
14½″ 1857
Standing, rifle in hand, beside a soldier with his left arm in a sling.

b HIGHLAND / JESSIE (raised caps.) 9″ 1857
Standing, beside a jug on a pedestal. On her right a soldier sitting.

Note. In both figures the soldier is probably Corp. Brown. There is nothing about a wounded soldier in her story.

6. ANGLO-FRENCH WAR SCARE, 1860

65. VOLUNTEER RIFLES

Napoleon III's annexation of Savoy and Nice aroused grave suspicions of his intentions, and caused a revival of the Volunteers. By the summer of 1860 130,000 had been enrolled, and the Queen reviewed 21,000 of them in Hyde Park.

a V. RIFLES (raised caps.) 12″ 1860 **Pl. 32**
An officer and soldier standing right and left of a clock face.

66. THE BRITISH LION

a NO TITLE 9″ 1860?
A large lion squatting on a French officer wearing an imperial (probably Napoleon III).

Note. This figure is found with their heads either on the left or the right.

7. AMERICAN CIVIL WAR (1861–5)

67. JOHN BROWN (1800–59)
An ardent abolitionist who in 1859 (two years before the war started) led an attack on the Federal Arsenal at Harper's Ferry, and was captured and hanged. The song, 'John Brown's Body' became almost the hymn of the Northern States.

a JOHN BROWN (raised caps.) 11″ 186– **Pl. 33**
A long-bearded man standing between two negro children.

68. ABRAHAM LINCOLN (1809–65)
President of the United States 1860–5

a A. LINCOLN (raised caps.) 15″ 186– **Pl. 34**
On horse facing left. Bare-headed.

NOTE

In 1852, nine years before the war, the publication of Mrs Beecher Stowe's *Uncle Tom's Cabin* and a play founded on it had aroused intense sympathy with the Abolitionists. Very many figures were made of the chief characters in the story, and it is probable that most of them originated before the war. Among the best are:

a UNCLE TOM (gilt script) 8¾″
Standing, bare-headed. His hat against his right foot; his right hand on a book resting on a corded package.

b AUNT CHLOE (gilt script) 8½″
Standing, a scarf over her head. A basket in her left hand.

c EVA & UNCLE TOM (gilt script) 8½″
Tom sitting, bare-headed, on a corded package, with an open book in his lap. To his right Eva standing, her hat in her right hand.

d (Five-line quotation, in black transfer (upper and lower case) of Eva and Tom's conversation, beginning '*Eva.* O Uncle Tom! What funny things you are making there!') 8½″.
Tom sitting on a rock, with a slate in both hands. To his left Eva standing on the rock. Both bare-headed.

e TOPSY & EVA (gilt script) 8½″
Both kneeling, bare-headed. Eva's right arm on Topsy's shoulders, and her left hand holding Topsy's right.

f GEORGE & ELIZA HARRIS (gilt script) 14″
Both standing bare-headed. George on the left, his hat in his right hand; between them a child in Eliza's arms.

8. THE RISORGIMENTO

69. GIUSEPPE GARIBALDI (1807–82)

The Liberator of Italy. In 1860 *invaded and conquered Sicily, and then landed on the mainland and conquered Naples. In* 1864 *visited England, and was welcomed with great popular enthusiasm.*

a GARIBALDI (gilt script) 19″ 1864 **Pl. 3**
Standing, bare-headed, in shirt and trousers. Right hand on sword hilt, left holding a paper. A cloak over left forearm, which rests on a round pedestal.

b GARIBALDI (raised caps.) 15″ 1864
As (a), but no cloak or paper, and a cloak draped against his right leg.

c LIBERTE (raised caps.) 13¼″ 1864 **Pl. 33**
Standing, dressed as (a). Left hand on sword hilt, right holding a pennon inscribed LIBERTE.

d NO TITLE 8½″ 1864
Standing, dressed as (a). Right hand on sword hilt, left on his belt; right forearm resting on a round pedestal; shells against his left leg.

e GARIBALDI (indented caps.) **Pl. 33**
12¼″ 1864
Standing, dressed as (a). Left hand tucked into shirt, right round the muzzle of his rifle.

Note. This may be a larger version of the GARIBALDI AT WAR, 9¼″ × 3½″, which appears in William Kent's earliest list (*c.* 1904), and which I have failed to find.

f GARIBALDI AT HOME (indented caps.) **Pl. 33**
9½″ 1864
Sitting, dressed as (a). Left hand holding spade between his legs; steeple hat beside his left foot.

g GARIBALDI (transfer black caps.) 14″ 186–
Standing, dressed as (a), beside his horse. His right arm on its shoulders.

The same design, 9″, is pair to 71a (Lord Napier).

h GARIBALDI (transfer black caps) 15″ 1864
On horse facing left. Dressed as (a). Right hand holds hat and reins on the horse's shoulders, left on its back.

Pair to 41d (K. of Sardinia).

i GARIBALDI (raised caps.) 15½″ 1864 **Pl. 34**
On horse facing right. In cocked hat, tunic, breeches and knee-boots.

Pair to 70a (Peard).

j GARIBALDI (raised caps.) 13½″ 1864 **Pl. 36**
Standing, bare-headed, in shirt, breeches, and
gaiters, a scarf over his shoulders. A flag to his
left, a gun to his right.
　　Pair to 70b (Peard).

WITH COLONEL PEARD

k GARIBALDI (raised caps.) 13″ 1864 **Pl. 36**
Left, Garibaldi (same design as (j)); *Right*,
Peard (same design as 70b). A watch-stand
between them.

70. COLONEL PEARD (1811–80)
'Garibaldi's Englishman', who joined him in 1860

*for the invasions of Sicily and Naples, and was so
like him that he impersonated him on one critical
occasion. Garibaldi visited Peard in England in
1864.*

See also 69k (Garibaldi)

a C. PEARD (raised caps.) 15″ 1864 **Pl. 34**
On horse facing left. In cocked hat, tunic,
breeches and knee-boots.
　　Pair to 69i (Garibaldi).

b C PEARD (raised caps.) 13¼″ 1864 **Pl. 36**
Standing, bare-headed, in shirt, breeches, and
gaiters, a scarf over his shoulders. A flag to his
right, a gun to his left.
　　Pair to 69j (Garibaldi).

9. ABYSSINIAN WAR, 1867

71. GENERAL LORD NAPIER OF MAGDALA (1810–90)
*Commanded the Abyssinian expedition of 1867
Created a Baron in 1868*

a NAPIER (transfer black caps.) 8½″ 1867 **Pl. 47**
Standing, bare-headed, in tunic, breeches,
and knee-boots, beside his horse. His left arm
on its shoulders.
　　Pair to a smaller size of 69g (Garibaldi).

10. FRANCO-PRUSSIAN WAR, 1870

72. KING WILLIAM I OF PRUSSIA (1797–1888)

*Succeeded his brother in 1861; proclaimed Em-
peror of Germany in 1871. Father of Prince
Frederick William, who also fought in this war
(see 4c).*

a KING OF PRUSSIA (gilt script) **Pl. 35**
15¾″ 1870
Standing, bare-headed, in uniform.
　　Pair to 73a (Q. of Prussia).

b KING OF PRUSSIA (raised caps & lower case)
12¾″ 1870 **Pl. 37**
On horse facing left. In helmet, tunic, and
knee-boots.
　　Pair to 78a (MacMahon).

73. QUEEN AUGUSTA OF PRUSSIA (1811–90)

*Daughter of the Grand Duke of Saxe-Weimar.
In 1829 married Prince William of Prussia (later
King and Emperor).*

a QUEEN OF PRUSSIA (gilt script) **Pl. 35**
16½″ 1870
Standing, bare-headed.
　　Pair to 72a (K. of Prussia).

74. PRINCE FREDERICK CHARLES OF PRUSSIA (1828–85)
*Nephew of King William I.
Army-Commander in the war*

a P F CHARLES (raised caps.) 14″ 1870 **Pl. 37**
On horse facing left. In helmet, uniform, and
knee-boots.
　　Same series as 75a (Bismarck) and 76a
(Moltke).

75. PRINCE BISMARCK (1815–98)
*The Chancellor of Prussia who determined
to have war with France in 1870*

a G : BISMARK (raised caps.) 14¾″ 1870 **Pl. 37**
On horse facing left. In helmet, uniform, and
knee-boots.

Same series as 74a (P. Fr. Charles) and 76a (Moltke).

76. COUNT VON MOLTKE (1800–91)

Prussian Field-Marshal; Chief of Staff of the Army for thirty years

a   G : MOLTKE (raised caps.)   14½″   1870   **Pl. 37**
On horse facing right. In helmet, uniform, and knee-boots.
    Same series as 74a (P. Fr. Charles) and 75a (Bismarck).

77. MARSHAL BAZAINE (1811–88)

In Aug. 1870 took over supreme command of the French Army, already in retreat, and brought it

back to Metz, where it surrendered on 14th October.

a   BAZAINE (raised caps.)   13½″   1870   **Pl. 37**
On horse facing left. In cocked hat.

78. MARSHAL MACMAHON (1806–93)

Marie Patrice Maurice MacMahon, Duke of Magenta; of Irish descent. Army Commander; wounded and taken prisoner. President of the French Republic 1873–9.

a   MAC MAHON (raised caps.)   11½″   1870   **Pl. 37**
On horse facing right. In cocked hat, tunic, cape, and knee-boots.
    Pair to 73b (K. of Prussia)

11. EGYPT AND THE SUDAN, 1882–5

79. LORD WOLSELEY (1833–1913)

In 1882 Sir Garnet Wolseley crushed the rebellion of the Egyptian army under Arabi Pasha, and was made a Baron. In 1884–5 he conducted the Nile campaign to relieve Gordon in Khartoum. Commander-in-Chief 1895–9.

a   SIR / G. WOLSELEY (raised caps.)   14″   1899
On horse facing right. In helmet, uniform, and knee-boots.
    Pair to 9a (D. of Connaught).

b   G. WOLSELEY (raised caps.)   12¾″   1882
On horse facing left. In helmet, uniform, and knee-boots.

c   WOLSELEY (indented caps.)   15″   1899
On horse facing right. In cocked hat, uniform, and knee-boots.
    Pair to 85b (Buller).

80. GENERAL GORDON (1833–85)

In 1884, as Governor-General of the Sudan, led the expedition to rescue the Egyptian garrisons there from the Mahdi's insurrection. The Mahdi surrounded him in Khartoum and, after a siege of 317 days, he was killed, Gladstone having delayed to send troops to rescue him.

a   GORDON (transfer caps. in crimson)   **Pl. 50**
16″   1885

Standing, in fez, uniform, and trousers. Left hand on the muzzle of a gun.

b   G. GORDON (raised caps.)   17¾″   1885
Standing, dressed as (a). Right hand on a tree trunk.

c   GENERAL GORDON (indented caps.)   **Pl. 40**
13¼″   1885
On camel facing left. In fez, close-fitting dress, and stockings.

81. MAJOR-GENERAL SIR HERBERT STEWART (1843–85)

Commanded the desert column in Wolseley's campaign to relieve Gordon. Died of wounds

a   G. STEWART (raised caps.)   14½″   1885
On horse facing right. In helmet, uniform, and knee-boots.
    Pair to 82a (Burnaby).

82. COLONEL F. G. BURNABY (1842–85)

Famous for his ride from Kazala to Khiva in 1875. Killed in Wolseley's campaign

a   C. BURNABY (raised caps.)   15″   1885
On horse facing left. In helmet, uniform, and knee-boots.
    Pair to 81a (Stewart).

NAVAL AND MILITARY

12. THE RIVER WAR, 1896–8

83. LORD KITCHENER OF KHARTOUM (1850–1916)

Sirdar of the Egyptian army 1890–9. Commander-in-Chief in the River War, and captured Khartoum 1898. In 1900 succeeded Lord Roberts as Commander-in-Chief in South Africa.

a THE SIRDAR (gilt script) 11″ 1898
On horse facing left. In topee and puttees.

b KITCHENER (indented caps.) 15″ 1898
On horse facing right. In a fez.
  Pair to 84b (MacDonald).

c LORD . KITCHENER (raised caps.) 12″ 1900
On horse facing right. In peaked cap.)
  Same series as 9b, 84c, 85a, 86a, 87a, & 88a.

d KITCHENER (raised caps.) 14″ 1900
Standing, in peaked cap, service dress, and gaiters.
  Pair to 86b (Roberts).

84. MAJOR-GENERAL SIR HECTOR MACDONALD (1853–1903)

In the River War, still with the substantive rank of Major, commanded an Egyptian brigade, and by his tactics at Omdurman turned a possible disaster into a victory. As 'Fighting Mac' he became a popular hero, partly because he had risen from the ranks. Promoted Major-General in 1900, he fought many successful actions in South Africa.

a MAJOR MACDONALD (gilt script) 14¼″ 1898
On horse facing left. In helmet, long tunic, and knee-boots.

b MACDONALD (indented caps.) 15″ 1898
On horse facing left. In cocked hat.
  Pair to 83b (Kitchener).

c HECTOR M^{AC}DONALD (raised caps.) 12½″ 1900
On horse facing left. In a busby.
  Same series as 9b, 83c, 85a, 86a, 87a, & 88a.

13. THE SOUTH AFRICAN WAR, 1899–1902

85. GENERAL SIR REDVERS BULLER (1839–1908)

Commander-in-Chief in South Africa from October to December 1899 when, after his defeat at Colenso, he was superseded by Lord Roberts.

a SIR REDVERS BULLER (raised caps.) 12″ 1899
On horse facing right. In peaked cap.
  Same series as 9b, 83c, 84c, 86a, 87a, & 88a.

b BULLER (indented caps.) 14¾″ 1899
On horse facing left. In peaked cap, knee-boots, etc.
  Pair to 79c (Wolseley).

86. LORD ROBERTS OF KANDAHAR (1832–1914)

Commander-in-Chief in South Africa from January to October 1900, when he returned to England, having saved the situation.

a LORD ROBERTS (raised caps.) 12¼″ 1900
One has been found with HANLEY/LANCASTERS LIMITED/ENGLAND stamped on its bottom.

On horse facing left. In low plumed helmet.
  Same series as 9b, 83c, 84c, 85a, 87a, & 88a.

b ROBERTS (raised caps.) 14″ 1900
Standing, in peaked cap, service dress, and gaiters.
  Pair to 83d (Kitchener).

c ROBERTS (indented caps.) 14½″ 1900
On horse facing left. In cocked hat.
  Pair to 87b (French).

87. GENERAL SIR JOHN FRENCH (1852–1925)

In 1899 commanded the mounted troops in Natal and cleared Cape Colony of the Boers

a GEN. FRENCH (raised caps.) 12″ 1900
On horse facing left. In helmet.
  Same series as 9b, 83c, 84c, 85a, 86a, & 88a.

b FRENCH (indented caps.) 15″ 1900
On horse facing right. In cocked hat.
  Pair to 86c (Roberts).

E

NAVAL AND MILITARY

88. COLONEL R. S. S. BADEN-POWELL (1857–1941)

In 1899–1900 was in command of Mafeking during its siege. In 1908 founded the Boy Scouts and Girl Guides.

a   BADEN-POWELL (raised caps.)   12″   1900
    On horse facing right. In slouch hat.
      Same series as 9b, 83c, 84c, 85a, 86a, & 87a.

b   BADEN-POWELL (gilt script)   16½″   1900
    Standing in slouch hat. Left hand on a gun.

c   BADEN-POWELL (indented caps.)   14½″   1900
    On horse facing right. In slouch hat.

89. THE PEACE, 1902

a   BOER WAR / PEACE DECLARED / JUNE 1   1902
    (raised caps.)   12½″   1902
    Behind, an Angel holding a ribbon inscribed
    PEACE ON EARTH GOOD WILL TOWARDS MEN
    (indented caps.).
    In front, left, a bearded Boer; *right,* John Bull,
    with a Union Jack waistcoat; both seated,
    shaking hands.
      Note. This horrible (post-Victorian) piece
    is based on a tolerable undated piece of the
    1880's or 1890's with the same angel standing
    behind two seated women, representing
    Ireland and Britannia. Their heads were cut
    off, and the Boer's and John Bull's stuck on,
    and their bodies appear to have been re-
    moulded while the clay was still soft.

(4) RELIGIOUS

90. ARCHBISHOP CRANMER (1489–1556)

Archbishop of Canterbury, 1533–56. Condemned for heresy by Cardinal Pole, and burnt at Oxford.

a ARCHBISHOP CRANMER (transfer caps.)
   9″ 1851   **Pl. 38**
   Standing in a pile of burning faggots. 'Burnt at Oxford / March 21 1556' (upper & lower case transfer) under the title.

91. BISHOPS RIDLEY (1500?–55) AND LATIMER (1485?–1555)

Nicholas Ridley, Bishop of London, and Hugh Latimer, Bishop of Worcester, were condemned for heresy and burnt at Oxford.

a RIDLEY AND LATIMER (transfer caps.) **Pl. 38**
   9½″ 1851
   Standing back to back, with the stake between them, among burning faggots. Under the title, 'Be of good comfort, Master Ridley, and play the man: we shall this day light such a candle, by God's grace, in England, as I trust shall never be put out' (u. & l. case transfer).

92. POPERY

a POPERY (transfer caps.) 9½″ 1851 **Pl. 38**
   A priest standing, bare-headed, in bands, soutane, and cloak. Right hand on a document, inscribed (u. & l. case transfer), 'Either we must root out the Bible or the Bible will root us out. The translators of the English Bible are to be abhorred to the depths of hell. It would be better to be without God's law than without the Pope.—Dr Troy, Archbishop of Dublin. 1816'.
   At the back is a flag inscribed (u. & l. case transfer), 'He that committeth his conscience to the keeping of another is no longer a free man. Freedom of conscience & freedom of thought are essential to the freedom of a nation. Therefore a nation of Catholics is a nation of Slaves.'
   Pair to 93a (Protestantism).

93. PROTESTANTISM

a PROTESTANTISM (transfer caps.)   **Pl. 38**
   9″ 1851
   A young woman standing, bare-headed, in a long dress, with bare feet. Right hand on a document inscribed (u. & l. case transfer), 'Search the Scriptures' John 5. 39. 'Prove all things', Thes. 5. 27. 'Let the word of Christ dwell in you richly'. C. 3. 16. 'To the Law and to the Testimony: if they speak not according to this word it is because there is no light in them' Isa. 8. 26.
   At the back is a flag inscribed (u. & l. case transfer), 'The Bible, the open Bible, is the Religion of Protestants. It is like every thing else from God free as the air we breathe. It spurns alike indulgences & Penance'.
   Pair to 92a (Popery).

94. £10000

a NO TITLE 9″ 1851   **Pl. 38**
   Left, a young woman standing. Right hand holds up a bag inscribed '£10000'; *Right*, a priest kneeling and holding out a veil towards her.
   Note. For the dating of these five anti-Catholic figures, see Ch. viii.

95. SAINT VINCENT DE PAUL (1576?–1660)

a Sᵀ VINCENT PAUL (indented caps.)   **Pl. 40**
   14¼″
   Standing, in skull-cap, soutane, and cloak; a child in his arms.

96. WILLIAM PENN (1644–1718)

Became a Quaker in 1667, and was imprisoned in the Tower of London 1668–9. In 1682 founded the colony of Pennsylvania.

a NO TITLE 8¼″   **Pl. 47**
   Standing, in broad-brimmed hat, long coat, breeches, and stockings. Right hand holds a deed, with seal attached, presumably the letters patent for his American lands.

RELIGIOUS

97. JOHN WESLEY (1703–91)

a   WESLEY (raised caps.)   11¼″   **Pl. 39**
Standing, bare-headed, in cassock and gown, in a Gothic niche.

     Almost identical, except the title, with 104a (Cooke).

b   WESLEY (raised caps.)   11¼″   **Pl. 39**
Half-length in a pulpit. Bare-headed, in bands and gown.

c   WESLEY (indented caps.)   7″
Standing, bare-headed, in bands, cassock, and gown, both hands holding an open book.

98. WILLIAM HUNTINGTON (1745–1813)

Good hearer and preacher; joined the Calvinistic Methodists in 1773. From 1783 to 1811 preached in chapels which he built in London. Licentious both before and after his conversion.

a   NO TITLE   8½″
     Sitting in an armchair. Bare-headed, in coat, high-cut waistcoat, breeches, and stockings. Left forearm on a book lying on a pedestal.

99. REV. CHRISTMAS EVANS (1766–1838)

Welsh farm-servant who became a preacher. In 1788 injured his right eye in a religious brawl. From 1792 to 1826 the very autocratic chief minister of all the Baptist churches in Anglesey.

     REV CHRISTMAS EVANS (raised caps.)   **Pl. 40**
     13½″
Standing, bare-headed, in swallow-tailed coat, breeches, and stockings. His right eye is closed.

100. REV. JOHN ELIAS (1774–1841)

Welsh Calvinistic Methodist preacher. In 1823 helped to draw up the Methodists' Articles of Faith

a   REV. JOHN ELIES. (raised caps.)   14″   **Pl. 39**
Standing, bare-headed, in long coat, breeches, and stockings.

101. WILLIAM O'BRYAN (1778–1868)

Expelled by the Methodists in 1810, in 1816 founded the Arminian Bible Christians. In 1831 emigrated to New York, but frequently revisited England.

a   J. BRYAN (raised caps.)   10½″   **Pl. 39**
Standing, bare-headed, very portly, in cut-away coat, breeches, and stockings.

Note. Mr Bernard Rackham, in his *Catalogue of the Glaisher Collection*, identified this figure as William O'Bryan.

102. DR THOMAS RAFFLES (1788–1863)

From 1811 to 1862 an independent minister in Liverpool; in 1839 Chairman of the Congregational Union. 'Tall and dignified, his voice and manner were suasive, and his power of anecdote suasive'. In the pulpit he wore bands, cassock, and gown.

a   DR RAFFLES (gilt script)   9½″   **Pl. 39**
Standing, bare-headed, in bands, cassock, and gown.

103. JOSEPH JOHN GURNEY (1788–1847)

Quaker minister and philanthropist, brother of Elizabeth Fry

a   J J GURNEY (gilt script)   11¼″   **Pl. 39**
Standing, bare-headed, in cut-away coat and trousers.

104. HENRY COOKE, D.D. (1788–1868)

Irish Presbyterian leader, but violently opposed to the disestablishment of the Irish Episcopal Church

a   COOKE D.D. (raised caps.)   10⅛″   **Pl. 39**
Standing, bare-headed, in a Gothic niche, in trousers (no cassock) and gown.

     Almost identical with 97a (Wesley).

105. POPE PIUS IX (1792–1878)

Reigned from 1846 to 1878

a   HIS HOLINESS THE POPE (gilt script)   **Pl. 41**
     17½″   187–
Standing, in skull-cap, knee-length coat, and trousers.

     Pair to 108a (Manning)?

106. SISTER MARGARET MARY HALLAHAN (1803–68)

A poor Irish servant who, in 1844, founded a community of Dominican Tertians in Coventry and, in 1851, a second community at Longton in the Potteries, which in 1853 she transferred to Stone. Founded the Hospital for Incurables at Stone.

a   NO TITLE   2¾″   c. 1850   **Pl. 41**
Standing, with hood over her head, in soutane and cloak. Her hands clasped under her scapular.

68

Note. This and 107a (Père Moulaert) were reproduced in the *Collector's Guide* for Jan. 1954, with caption, 'Friar and Nun, believed to be Père Moulaert and Sister Margaret Hallahan. The pair once belonged to Captain Mayo, who as a young midshipman in John Company won the V.C. during the Mutiny, *aet.* 17. He was given them about 1850 by his old nurse'.

107. PERE BERNARD MOULAERT
(1808–70)

Belgian Dominican, Librarian of the Monastery at Tirlemont. About 1850 worked for a time at Longton with Sister Hallahan.

a   NO TITLE $3\frac{1}{4}''$ *c.* 1850   **Pl. 41**
Standing, in round hat, soutane, and cloak. His arms crossed over his chest.
Pair to 106a (Hallahan).

108. CARDINAL MANNING (1808–92)

1840, Archdeacon of Chichester; 1851, joined the Roman Church; 1865, Archbishop of Westminster; 1875, Cardinal. Strong supporter and intimate of Pius IX.

a   CARDINAL MANNING (gilt script)   **Pl. 41**
$17\frac{3}{4}''$ *c.* 1875
Standing, in biretta, chasuble, and soutane.
Pair to 105a (Pius IX)?

109. REV. EDWARD MEYRICK GOULBURN, D.D. (1818–97)

The only recorded copy of this figure of a preacher in his pulpit is titled COULBURN *in gilt script. This surname (with a C) cannot be found in the D.N.B., in the B. M. Library Catalogue, nor in the current London Telephone Directory, and the Librarian of the Evangelical Library can find no record of a minister of this name. It seems probable that the C is a mistake for G, and that the figure represents Dr E. M. Goulburn, Headmaster of Rugby School, 1849–57, and Dean of Norwich, 1866–97, who was a celebrated preacher and, between 1854 and 1862, published three devotional books which ran into many editions. If so, it is the only known example of a figure of a contemporary Church of England clergyman, popular perhaps because he started as an Evangelical, though later he became a High Churchman.*

a   COULBURN (gilt script) $11\frac{1}{2}''$ **Pl. 51**
Half-length; standing, bare-headed, in a pulpit. In choker, low-cut waistcoat, and jacket.

110. GENERAL BOOTH (1829–1912)

In 1865 started the Christian Mission in Whitechapel; in 1878 it became the Salvation Army

a   NO TITLE $14''$ 189–   **Pl. 4**
Head and shoulders (no pedestal), in Salvation Army hat and uniform. THE SALVATION ARMY on his hat-band, a crowned device, inscribed BLOOD AND FIRE, on his jersey, and crowned devices, inscribed S, on his coat-collar and shoulder straps, all in gold, probably hand-painted. A cast figure.

111. REV. CHARLES SPURGEON
(1834–92)

Baptist preacher. Came to London at the age of twenty, and two years later Exeter Hall was not large enough to hold his hearers. From 1861 till his death ministered at the Metropolitan Tabernacle, which held six thousand.

a   C H SPURGEON (raised caps.)   **Pl. 43**
$12\frac{1}{2}''$ *c.* 1856
Standing, bare-headed, in frock coat, low-cut waistcoat, and trousers.

b   CH SPURGEON (raised caps.) $11\frac{1}{2}''$ **Pl. 39**
Half-length, standing in a pulpit, bare-headed.

c   C H / SPURGEON (raised caps.) $11\frac{3}{4}''$
Same design as (b), but the outlines of the pulpit are straight lines instead of graceful curves, and its base is solid instead of having two openings.

112. DWIGHT LYNAM MOODY
(1837–99)

American revivalist preacher who came to England 1873–5, 1881–4, and 1891–2

a   MOODY (raised caps.) $17''$ 187–   **Pl. 42**
Standing, bare-headed, with long beard.
Pair to 113a (Sankey).

113. IRA D. SANKEY (1840–1908)

Accompanied Moody on his visits to England to lead the hymn-singing

a   SANKEY (raised caps.) $17''$ 187–   **Pl. 42**
Standing, bare-headed, with moustache and whiskers.
Pair to 112a (Moody).

(5) AUTHORS

114. WILLIAM SHAKESPEARE
(1564–1616)

a SHAKSPERE (raised caps.) 10¾"
Standing, bare-headed, in cloak, doublet, breeches, and stockings. Right elbow on four books lying on a pedestal decorated with two heads, right hand almost touching right cheek; left hand holds a rolled paper, right leg crossed over the left at the knee
　　Based on the statue by Scheemaker in Westminster Abbey.
　　Pair to 116a (Milton).

b SHAKESPEARE (gilt script) 18½"
As (a), but only three books and no heads on the pedestal, a paper hangs from its top, and his left hand holds a book against his left hip.

c NO TITLE 14½"
As (b), but left hand almost touches the pedestal and holds no book, and the pedestal is decorated with S's and reversed S's, and has only two books on it.

d SHAKSPEARE (raised caps.) 14¾"
As (b), but no book in his left hand, no paper on the pedestal, and legs not crossed.

e SHAKS / PEARE (raised caps.) 14"
As (b), but left hand empty, and resting on the pedestal. Standing under an arch with a pointed canopy.

f NO TITLE 12½"
Standing, dressed as in (a). Left forearm on three books lying on a pedestal; a paper in his left hand, and his right hand touching it, left leg crossed over right.

g NO TITLE 9"
As (f), but only two books, and right hand points at the paper, but does not touch it.
　　Pair to 116b (Milton).

h NO TITLE 7"
Sitting, bare-headed, in doublet, breeches, and stockings. Left hand holds an open book in his lap, right hand holds a pen above it. A large jar standing to his left; left foot on a closed book.

i NO TITLE 10½"
Above a clock, Shakespeare standing, dressed as in (a). Left forearm on three books on a pedestal. *Left of the clock*, Hamlet sitting, in high-plumed hat, doublet, breeches, and stockings, a cloak over his right shoulder; *Right of the clock*, Lady Macbeth? sitting, in crown, low-necked dress, and cloak (see note on 116i).

j NO TITLE 11"
Above a clock, Shakespeare as in (i). *Left of the clock*, Tragedy sitting, a scarf over her head; *Right*, Comedy sitting, bare-headed, a paper in her right hand.
　　Note. Closely resembles a clockcase, designed by Bell and made in Minton's Parian ware, which was exhibited at the Society of Arts' Exhibition of British Manufactures in 1848. (Engraving in *Ill. Lon. News*, 18 March 1848.)

WITH MILTON

k NO TITLE 9"
Clock in the middle. *Left*, Milton standing, left arm on two books, right holding a third against his side; *Right*, Shakespeare standing, right forearm on two books, a manuscript in each hand.

115. SHAKESPEARE'S HOUSE

a SHAKESPERE'S HOUSE (gilt script) 5" **Pl. 49**
A two-storied cottage, with one door and three windows, a thatched roof, and two chimney stacks.
　　Note. Represents the birthplace at Stratford-on-Avon as it was before the restorations of 1857–8.

116. JOHN MILTON (1608–74)
See also 114k (Shakespeare)

a MILTON (raised caps.) 11¼"
Standing, bare-headed, in doublet, breeches, and stockings. Left hand, holding a paper,

rests on three books on a round pedestal, right hand holds up a corner of his cloak across him.

Pair to 114a (Shakespeare).

b NO TITLE 9″
Standing, bare-headed, dressed as (a). Left elbow on a pedestal; right hand holding a book against his leg; cloak over his right shoulder.

Pair to 114g (Shakespeare).

117. VOLTAIRE (1694–1778)

a NO TITLE 9¾″   **Pl. 46**
Standing, bare-headed, in long coat, waistcoat, breeches and stockings.

b VOLTAIRE (script caps.) 3½″
Head and neck, above an ink-well.

118. ROBERT BURNS (1759–96)

a ROB^t BURNS (raised caps.) 13½″   **Pl. 43**
Standing, bare-headed, in long coat, breeches, and stockings, a plaid over his shoulders, and bonnet in his left hand.

b R. BURNS (raised caps.) 11½″   **Pl. 43**
Standing, bare-headed, in long coat and trousers.

Pair to 120a (Scott).

c R BURNS (gilt script) 10½″
Standing, bare-headed, in long coat, breeches, and gaiters, a plaid over his left shoulder. Reads a book held in his left hand.

Pair to a smaller size (10¾″) of 120b (Scott).

Note. Probably there was a larger figure of this design as a pair to the 14¾″ Scott.

d NO TITLE 9¾″ 1844
Standing, bare-headed, in coat, breeches, and stockings, a plaid over his left shoulder and draped across him. A scroll in his left hand, flowers in his right.

From an engraving in *Ill. Lon. News* of 10 Aug. 1844, illustrating the Burns Festival at Ayr on August 6th.

e NO TITLE 7½″ *c.* 1848   **Pl. 7**
Sitting, bare-headed, a snuff-box in his right hand.

Note. Clearly belongs to the 'Alpha' factory group of *c.* 1848. The clothes show that it does not represent a contemporary, but both they and the head closely resemble the figures of Burns (a), (b) & (c).

f R BURNS / BORN JANUARY 25 / 1759 / DIED JULY 21 / 1796 (gilt script) 15¾″ 1882? **Pl. 33**
Standing, in bonnet, long coat, breeches, and stockings. On a high round pedestal, inscribed under its base, 'Sampson Smith / Longton Staff / England / 1882' (indented u. & l. case).

WITH HIGHLAND MARY

g BURNS / AND HIS / MARY (raised caps.)
12″   **Pl. 22**
Standing, bare-headed, with his left arm round Mary's shoulders. A tree (spill-holder) behind him.

Note. Mr B. Latham has a copy marked 'S. Smith / Longton / 1851'.

h BURNS & H^D MARY (raised caps.) 12″
Under an arch of bare boughs Burns and Mary, 4½″ to 5″ high, sit on rocks above a river. *Right*, Burns in bonnet, plaid, long coat and breeches; *Left*, Mary, bare-headed. A dog in the foreground.

i NO TITLE 11¼″
Both sitting in front of a tree (spill-holder). *Left*, Burns, in bonnet, coat, and trousers, with his left arm round Mary's shoulders.

Below them eight lines of the poem, 'How sweetly blessed the gay green birk' (gilt u. & l. case).

Some copies are inscribed with other verses.

j BURNS & HIS / HIGHLAND MARY (raised caps.) 10¾″
Burns, on the left, and Mary, on the right, both in Highland costume and standing with their right hands clasped.

119. HIGHLAND MARY (*c.* 1768–86)

Burns dedicated some of his finest poems to her, but nothing certain is known of her. She is said to have been the daughter of a Clyde sailor, Archibald Campbell.

See also 118g, h, i & j (Burns)

a HIGHLAND / MARY (raised caps.) 17″ **Pl. 35**
Standing, her plaid over her head, in a short dress, with bare feet.

Note. An excellent piece, to which presumably there was a pair of Burns, but none has yet been found.

120. SIR WALTER SCOTT (1771–1832)

a S. W. SCOTT (raised caps.) 12″   **Pl. 43**

Standing, bare-headed, in swallow-tail coat and trousers.

Pair to 118a (Burns).

b SIR WALTER SCOTT (gilt script) 14¾"
Standing, dressed as in (a), with plaid over his left shoulder, and a dog sitting on his right.

In a smaller size, 10¾", pair to 118c (Burns).

121. LORD BYRON (1788–1824)

a L. BYRON (indented caps.) 7½" c. 1848 **Pl. 7**
Sitting, bare-headed, in jacket and loose trousers, a cloak over his shoulders.

b BYRON (raised caps.) 16½" **Pl. 33**
Standing, bare-headed, in Greek dress.

c NO TITLE 8"
Sitting, bare-headed, above a clock-face, in jacket, waistcoat, and loose trousers, a cloak over his shoulders.

WITH THE MAID OF ATHENS

d BYRON & MAID OF ATHENS (gilt script) 13½"
Sitting, bare-headed, in open-necked shirt, jacket, breeches, and knee-boots. Left arm round the Maid's shoulders. She sits, in a cap and long dress. Her head resting on her left hand.

122. LETITIA ELIZABETH LANDON
(1802–38)

As 'L. E. L.' published poems and novels from 1820 to her death. Collected editions of her poems were published in 1850 and 1873.

Engravings of 'L. E. L.', (1) after H. W. Pickersgill by C. Cook, undated, (2) after D. Maclise by J. B. Forrest, frontispiece to The Poetical Works of Miss Landon *(Philadelphia, 1838), show her with a similar hair-style to this figure.*

a NO TITLE 7⅝" **Pl. 32**
Sitting, bare-headed, on a one-ended sofa. Right hand holds a little open book in her lap.

123. ELIZA COOK (1818–89)

A very popular poetess. Published Lays of a Wild Harp *in 1835, and* Eliza Cook's Journal *from 1849 to 1854.*

a ELIZA COOK (indented caps.) 10¾" **Pl. 46**
Standing, bare-headed, with long ringlets; a closed book in her right hand.

(6) STAGE

124. JAMES QUIN (1693–1766)

From 1716 to 1751 played leading parts in London, especially in tragedy

a FALSTAFF (raised caps.) 17″ **Pl. 35**
Standing, in a round hat, long coat and waistcoat, and high boots. His sword-hilt in his right hand.

Copied from a porcelain figure, after an undated mezzotint of Quin by James MacArdell, first made (*c.* 1766) by the Derby Factory, which produced it in six sizes before 1800. This earthenware figure is a close copy of the second (15¼″) version, in which Quin is clean-shaven; other versions give him a beard and moustaches. It is the only one which bears a title. By 1850, though Quin was forgotten, this had become the traditional representation of the most popular of Shakespearean characters. (From information supplied by Messrs Mander & Mitchenson.)

125. DAVID GARRICK (1717–79)

a RICHARD THE THIRD (gilt script) **Pl. 45**
9¾″
Sitting on a couch in a tent (*K. Rd. III*, act v, sc. 3).

This, and all Staffordshire figures of Garrick, is based on Hogarth's painting 'David Garrick as Richard III' (1745), now in the Walker Art Gallery, Liverpool.

The right hand, left leg, and head were made from subsidiary moulds, and therefore vary slightly in position from one figure to another.

Note. The title EDMUND KEAN which appears on an 8″ version of this figure in Pl. 44 of Mr Bryan Latham's *Victorian Staffordshire Portrait Figures* is a very recent addition.

b NO TITLE 7″
The same design as (a), but made from one two-piece mould and much simplified. He wears boots instead of shoes, and no garter.

126. JOHN PHILIP KEMBLE (1757–1823)

His first great success was as Hamlet in Dublin in

1781, *and his first appearance in London was in the same part at Drury Lane in* 1783.

a NO TITLE 8¾″ 184–
Standing, in round hat with two plumes, short trunks and hose, a cloak over both shoulders. A broad ribbon passes from his right shoulder across his tunic. Left hand holds a skull, and right hand points to it.

From an engraving of Sir Thomas Lawrence's painting now in the National Portrait Gallery.

b NO TITLE 8½″ 184–
Same design as (a), but the hat has three plumes, and the cloak is edged with ermine.

Note. There is a pair to this, of a woman standing, crowned and in an ermine-edged cloak, a handkerchief in her left hand. This probably represents Lady Macbeth (possibly Kemble's sister, Mrs Siddons), she and Hamlet being the principal male and female characters of the Shakespearean drama, as in 114h (Shakespeare).

c NO TITLE 8″
Right, Hamlet as in (b); *Left*, Woman (Lady Macbeth?) as in Note to (b).

d ALAS POOR YORICK (gilt or black transfer)
11¼″ *c.* 1852 **Pl. 45**
Standing, as in (a), but the hat has only one plume, the cloak hangs more behind him, and there is no broad ribbon across his tunic.

From the later engraving after Lawrence's portrait in Tallis' *Shakespeare Gallery*, entitled 'John Philip Kemble as Hamlet / Alas, poor Yorick. / Act 5, sc. 1'.

e HAMLET (indented caps.) 11″ *c.* 1852
As in (d), but the cloak is only over his left shoulder.

f NO TITLE 12″
Same design as (d), but he wears breeches instead of short trunks.

127. WILLIAM CHARLES MACREADY (1793–1873)

'*The most romantic of actors*' (Talfourd). First appearance was as Romeo in Birmingham in 1810.

In 1819 *his Richard III raised him to the top of his profession. He retired in* 1851.

a MACREADY (gilt script) 8″ **Pl. 47**
Standing, bare-headed and bearded, in a long coat, short trunks, and stockings.

From a 'Id plain, 2d coloured' theatrical print of Macready as Richard III.

b SHYLOCK (indented caps.) 9¾″ *c.* 1852 **Pl. 45**
Standing, bearded and long-haired, in high hat and long dress.

From the engraving, after a painting by Tracey, in Tallis' *Shakespeare Gallery*, entitled 'Mr Macready as Shylock / Merchant of Venice. Act i, sc. 3'.

Note. The figure in Plate 45 is a smaller version (7″).

c MACBETH (indented caps.) **Pl. 43**
8¼″ *c.* 1852
Standing, in plumed bonnet, in knee-length frock; a shield over his left arm.

From the engraving by Sherratt, after a painting by Tracey, in Tallis' *Shakespeare Gallery*, entitled 'Mr Macready as Macbeth / Act I, sc. 3'.

Pair to a smaller size of 135a (Glyn), 8″.

Note. It is probable that this figure was also made about 10″ as a pair to the larger version of Lady Macbeth (Isabella Glyn).

128. LUIGI LABLACHE (1794–1858)

Operatic bass, born at Naples. In 1848 *sang many times at Drury Lane with Jenny Lind. Here represented as Dr Dulcamara in Donizetti's L'Elisir d'Amore.*

a NO TITLE 8½″ 1848? **Pl. 52**
Standing, bare-headed, in stock, and tail-coat.

From a coloured lithograph music-front by John Brandard to *Operatic Celebrities* (a series of six selections), published in 1848, in which he holds a philtre instead of a piece of music. (Identified by Messrs Mander & Mitchenson.)

129. JAMES HENRY HACKETT
(1800–71)

American actor, born in New York. In 1827 *appeared in London with Yankee stories and imitations of Edmund Kean. Came again* 1832, 1840, 1845, *and* 1851 *and frequently played Falstaff.*

a FALSTAFF (indented caps.) **Pl. 45**
9½″ *c.* 1852

Standing, bearded, in broad-brimmed hat, long coat and loose trousers. His right hand resting on a stick.

From the engraving, after a daguerrotype by Haas of New York, in Tallis' *Shakespeare Gallery*, entitled 'Mr Hackett as Falstaff / K. Hen. iv, Pt. I, Act 4, sc. 2'.

130. EDWARD MORGAN (b. 179–?)

In 1825 *Charles James Mathews wrote 'A Song of Jenny Jones and Ned Morgan', who were then dairymaid and ploughman at Pontblyddin Farm, near Llangollen. Morgan had come back after twenty years in the Navy to marry Jenny. In* 1836 *Mathews included his song in his one-act farce,* He would be an actor, *produced at the Olympic Theatre. For the next twenty years the song and its theme were immensely popular. (See The Life of Charles James Mathews, by Charles Dickens, junior,* 1879.)

a EDWARD MORGAN (gilt script) 11½″ **Pl. 52**
Standing, in sailor's dress, his left hand holding a jug on a stool, his right hand holding a mug above his head.

From an undated lithograph, 'Edward Morgan', by E. Walker and J. C. Rowland, of which there is a print at Plas Newydd.

Note. There is a companion lithograph of Jenny Jones, but no figure of her has been found.

131. ISAAC VAN AMBURGH (1811–65?)

American animal-tamer, born in Kentucky. In 1839 *appeared at Drury Lane with his mixed cage of lions, leopards, and a lamb. Queen Victoria attended three performances in one fortnight, and the Duke of Wellington commissioned Landseer to paint 'Van Amburgh and the Lions'. He came to England again in* 1843 *and* 1848.

a MR VAN AMBURGH (gilt script) **Pl. 48**
6″ *c.* 1840
Standing, bare-headed and bearded, in a short-skirted dress, among his animals.

b NO TITLE 12¾″ 1848 **Pl. 47**
Standing, dressed as in (a), with a shawl over his shoulders. His right hand on the lower jaw of a lion. The lion on its hind legs.

Much resembles in reverse the engraving 'Van Amburgh at Vauxhall Gardens' in *Ill. Lon. News*, 2 Sept. 1848.

Note. Messrs Mander & Mitchenson warn me that they have many reasons for thinking that the figure represents 'Samson and the Lion'.

132. LOUIS ANTOINE JULLIEN
(1812–60)

French conductor and impresario. From 1842 to 1859 gave winter seasons of excellent promenade concerts at Covent Garden and the English Opera House. In 1847 started an opera season at Drury Lane, but soon went bankrupt.

a   JULLIEN (indented caps.)   8″   *c.* 1848   **Pl. 7**
Standing, bare-headed and bearded, in swallow-tail coat.
   Note. This figure is also found with the title in gilt script.

133. CHARLOTTE CUSHMAN (1816–76) & SUSAN CUSHMAN (1822–59)

Charlotte, 'the most powerful actress America has produced', and Susan, 'a pretty creature', were born at Boston. In 1845 they came to England, and appeared in December as Romeo and Juliet at the Princess theatre, and subsequently in the country. They remained in England till 1849, and were again here from 1852 to 1857.

a   *Jul.* O think'st thou we shall ever meet again?
   Rom. I doubt it not; and all these woes shall serve
      For sweet discourse in our time to come.
   (transfer u. & l. case)   10½″   *c.* 1852   **Pl. 16**
Left, Romeo, in skirted tunic; *Right*, Juliet, in tight bodice and full skirt. Both standing, bare-headed.
   After the engraving, of a painting (1845) by Margaret Gillies, in Tallis' *Shakespeare Gallery*, *entitled* 'CHARLOTTE AND SUSAN CUSHMAN / as ROMEO AND JULIET / Act 3 sc. 5'.

134. JENNY LIND (1820–87)

Swedish singer. In 1847 appeared in London as Alice in Meyerbeer's opera Robert le Diable. During the next two years appeared in many operas, including Donizetti's La Figlia del Reggimento, and at many concerts. Returned to England in 1855, *and made a triumphant concert tour in England, Scotland and Wales.*

AS ALICE IN ROBERT LE DIABLE

a   JENNY LIND AS ALICE IN MEYERBEERS OPERA (gilt script)   13½″   *c.* 1847   **Pl. 44**
Kneeling, bare-headed, her arms round the Pedestal of a Celtic Cross. The pedestal is decorated with vine leaves, and the Cross faces to the front.
   From a lithograph by and after T. Packer.

b   NO TITLE   11″   *c.* 1847
As (a), but right arm round the Cross, left hand on the front of the pedestal. A decorative base with a ribbon on it, perhaps intended for a script title.

c   NO TITLE   9″   *c.* 1847
As (a), but right hand on the back of the Cross, left on the front of the pedestal, and the Cross faces half-right.

d   JENNY LIND (gilt script)   10″   *c.* 1847   **Pl. 45**
Standing, bare-headed. Right hand on the side of the Cross, left on top of the pedestal.

AS MARIA IN LA FIGLIA DEL REGGIMENTO

e   JENNY LIND AS MARIA (gilt script)   **Pl. 45**
10½″   *c.* 1847
Standing, in low-crowned, broad-brimmed hat.
   From the music front, by John Brandard, to 'The Songs from La Figlia del Reggimento'.

f   M. LIND (indented caps.)   8″   *c.* 1847   **Pl. 7**
Standing, hat as in (e); Right hand raised to its brim.
   From the music front, by John Brandard, to 'La Vivandière Quadrille'.
   Note. This figure is also found as in *Pl.* 7, with the title in gilt script.

g   JENNY LIND (indented caps.)   **Pl. 7**
7¾″   *c.* 1847
Standing, bare-headed, in the costume she wore in Act 2. Both hands holding a piece of music.

AS CONCERT SINGER

h   JENNY LIND (gilt script)   8¼″   **Pl. 46**
Standing, bare-headed; long skirt with one flounce. Reticule in right hand.

i   JENNY LIND (gilt script)   8″   **Pl. 46**
Standing, bare-headed. Both hands in front of her waist.

135. ISABELLA GLYN (1823–89)

Made début as Constance in King John *in 1847. Played Shakespearean parts at Sadler's Wells from 1848 to 1851.*

a LADY MACBETH (indented caps.) 10" **Pl. 45**
Standing, bare-headed. Handkerchief in her right hand.

From the engraving, after a daguerrotype, in Tallis' *Shakespeare Gallery*, entitled 'Miss Glyn as Lady Macbeth / Act I, sc. 5'.

Pl. 45 illustrates a smaller version, 8", pair to 127c (Macready).

136. EDWARD ASKEW SOTHERN (1826–81)

In 1861, at the Haymarket, appeared as Lord Dundreary, a brainless peer, in Tom Taylor's Our American Cousin, *and in its revivals in 1863, 1867, and 1878. Dundreary whiskers and clothes became a fashion.*

a NO TITLE 8½" 1861 **Pl. 45**
Standing, bare-headed, with long whiskers, in frock coat, a monocle in his right eye. His right hand is counting the number of his relations on the palm of his left.

From a photograph of the first production, which was also used for a lithograph music front.

137. JENNY MARSTON (c. 1830–61) & FREDERICK ROBINSON (1830–1912)

As Perdita and Florizel in Phelps' revival of The Winter's Tale *at Sadler's Wells in July 1851*

a WINTER'S TALE (indented caps.) **Pl. 16**
11¾" c. 1852
Perdita, bare-headed, in a long dress; Florizel, a ribbon round his hair, in skirted tunic. Behind them a tree trunk.

From an engraving by Sherratt, after a daguerrotype by Paine of Islington, in Tallis' *Shakespeare Gallery*, entitled 'Miss Jenny Marston and Mr F Robinson / Act 4, sc. 3'.

Note. There was no engraving of Ophelia in the *Shakespeare Gallery*, and the 'Tallis' factory's OPHELIA (indented caps. 10¼") in Plate 45 was copied from this figure of Jenny Marston.

138. ELLEN BRIGHT (1832–50)

Niece of George Wombwell, and at 16 became 'The Lion Queen' in his menagerie. A year later, on 11 Jan. 1850, when performing at Chatham in a cage with a lion and a tiger, she was mauled to death by the tiger.

a DEATH OF THE LION QUEEN (gilt script)
15" 1850 **Pl. 33**
Standing, in plumed hat and short skirt. A lion behind her to her right, a leopard to her left on its hind legs with its forelegs on her waist.

Note. An untitled figure, 11¾", in the same style is of a girl in similar clothes, with a hoop on her right arm, between a lion and a tiger. As Ellen Bright was 'The Lion Queen' for so short a time, this is likely to represent her predecessor, Nellie Chapman, another niece of Wombwell, who married 'Lord' George Sanger in 1849. She had appeared before Queen Victoria at Windsor in 1847.

139. JOHN SOLOMON RAREY (1827–66)

American horse-tamer. Came to England in 1857. Exhibited before the Queen and Prince Albert at Windsor, and toured all over Europe. In 1860 returned to America with 'Cruiser', an English thoroughbred stallion notorious for his ferocity until Rarey, in response to a public challenge in London, broke his spirit by leaving him all night with his forelegs tied and his hind legs drawn up and tied to a collar put over his head.

a RAREY (gilt script) 9¼" 1860 **Pl. 52**
Horse facing left, a cloak over his saddle. In front of him Rarey standing.

(7) SPORT

140. BENJAMIN CAUNT (1815–61)

Pugilist. Styled 'Champion of England' after defeating John Leechman ('Brassey') in 1840

a BEN CAUNT (raised caps.) 15½″ 1844
Bust, 11″. Bare-headed with fringe beard, in high collar, bow tie, coat and waistcoat. *Pedestal,* 4½″, round, shelving to a high round base. On the top layer the title in front, and at the back BY H BENTLEY MODELED FROM LIFE 1844 (indented caps.) On the shelved part a belt, presented to him in 1841, is moulded. On the base, in three columns, a list of his fights won or lost (indented caps.)
(No. 1030 in the Willett Collection, Brighton.)

141. JOHN CARMEL HEENAN (1835–73) & TOM SAYERS (1826–65)

Heenan, 'The Benicia Boy', born in New York State; in 1859 married Adah Menken. Sayers, a London bricklayer, started boxing in 1849, and won the Champion's Belt in 1857. On 17 April 1860 they fought at Farnborough before 12,000 spectators. Heenan, fourteen stone and more than six ft., repeatedly knocked down Sayers, of medium size. In the thirty-seventh round the police interfered, and the umpires declared a draw.

a HEENAN SAYERS (raised caps.) **Pl. 47**
9¾″ 1860
Each, bare to the waist, with his fist in the other's face. Their different heights are not represented.

142. FULLER PILCH (1803–70)

A Norfolk man, but from 1836 to 1854 played cricket for Kent; till 1850, at least, the supreme English batsman.

a NO TITLE 7½″ 1843 **Pl. 52**
Standing, in top-hat, shirt, and trousers, batting right-handed. Behind him a wicket and a tree trunk (spill-holder).
From an engraving in the *Ill. Lon. News* of 15 July 1843, illustrating its report of the Kent

v. All England match, for many years the chief event of the cricket season.
Pair to 143a (Box).

143. THOMAS BOX (1809–76)

Played for Sussex, his native county; the greatest wicket-keeper of his time. A constant member of William Clarke's All England XI.

a NO TITLE 6½″ 1843 **Pl. 52**
Standing over the wicket, in top-hat, shirt, and trousers. Tree trunk (spill-holder), behind him.
From an engraving in *Ill. Lon. News* of 15 July 1843 (see above).
Pair to 142a (Pilch).
Note. The different heights of these two figures may be because Pilch was 6 ft. and Box only 5 ft. 7.

144. CRICKETERS

a NO TITLE 14″ **Pl. 25**
Standing, in round-topped cap, with a fringe beard except under his chin. A ball in his right hand; to his left a bat leant against a wicket.
Pair to (b).

b NO TITLE 14″ **Pl. 25**
Standing, in a close-fitting cap, clean-shaven except for a moustache. Holding a bat in both hands.
Pair to (a).
There is also a 10½″ figure of this design, but none of (a) has been found.

Mr Falcke, the antique dealer who specialised in cricket prints and figures, told me that he had never seen either of these figures with a title[1], but that there was a tradition that (a) represented George Parr and (b) Julius Caesar. This identification of (a) is supported by John C. Anderson's engraving of Parr in *Sketches at Lords* (1852), in which he has similar hair, fringe beard, and square face. It was, and still is, common to indicate the Captain in a cricket group by giving him both bat and ball; by 1857 (the period to which these figures appear to belong) Parr was Captain of All England.

No evidence has been found for the identification of (b) as Julius Caesar, but both Parr and Caesar were famous all over England as members of William Clarke's All England XI, which for many years toured all over the country playing local sides. Parr played for it from its start in 1846 till 1870, succeeding Clarke as its Captain in 1857, and Caesar played for it from 1849 to 1867. Parr was also Captain of the All England teams to the U.S.A. and Canada in 1859, and to Australia in 1863. W. G. Grace, in his *Cricket* (1891), called Parr the best batsman of his age; 'his name was on the lips of every player for twenty years'. Caesar too was a great batsman, and for many years made large scores for Surrey, the Players, and All England. He went with Parr's teams to America and Australia.

[1] Plate 70 in Mr B. Latham's *Victorian Staffordshire Portrait Figures* shows (a) with a script title 'Alfred Mynn', but this title, written on paper, had only recently been stuck on it. The designer of a figure of Mynn would hardly have failed to suggest his famous bulk (6′ 1″ tall, and 18 to 19 stone in his heyday); Parr, 5′ 9″, and Caesar, 5′ 7½″, were more normal.

145. CAPTAIN MATTHEW WEBB
(1848–83)

Captain in the mercantile marine. In August 1875 he swam the Channel from Dover to Calais, the first to perform this feat, in twenty-two hours. He was drowned in an attempt to swim Niagara.

a NO TITLE 5¾″ 1875 **Pl. 48**
An enormous head, facing half-right, in a straw hat (a detachable lid), and a small tapering body, in striped shirt with a broad collar, knotted tie, and trousers. His elbows rest on a flat corded bundle, which may represent a bale of corks.

Instead of swimming he seems to be floating comfortably. The bundle has a W (or possibly M) on top, and a C on its front side, and there is also a mark ←⊖→ top on which seems to indicate that he is in transit.

There can be little doubt from his features, nautical clothes and these signs that the figure is a caricature of Webb.

146. GRAPPLERS

In an ancient Scandinavian form of duel (Baeltespaennare) the combatants were stripped and bound together by a leather belt, and fought to the death with short-bladed knives. This figure is a copy of a large bronzed-zinc statue by J. P. Molin which was lent by Sweden to the London International Exhibition of 1862, and 'attracted nearly unanimous admiration' (Ill. Lon. News, 1 Nov. 1862, which has an engraving of it).

The statue now stands in front of the National Museum, Stockholm.

a GRAPPLERS (raised caps.) 11½″ **Pl. 47**
Two naked men bound together by a belt round their waists, each armed with a short knife in his right hand.

147. 'JUMBO' (1863–85)

An African elephant which the Zoo obtained in 1865 by exchange with the Jardin des Plantes, Paris. He was then from 1½ to 2 years old, and 4 ft. high. He became a great favourite with the public, but in 1881 he became dangerous, and in 1882, in spite of public protests, he was sold to Barnum, the American showman. He was then 11 ft. 6 ins. high, and weighed 6 tons. In 1885 he died in Ontario from the effects of charging a train.

a JUMBO (raised caps.) 10½″
Standing, facing right, with no trappings. Tusks only ¼″; trunk, with its end curled, touching the ground. A tree trunk supports his belly.

148. 'MASTER McGRATH' (c. 1866–1871)

A black greyhound, belonging to Lord Lurgan; won the Waterloo Cup three times, in 1868, 1869 and 1871. His owner received the Queen's command to take him to Windsor for her inspection.

'The most famous dog that ever lived. His name was known in the humblest cottage, his deeds were celebrated in song and ballad, his picture was to be seen everywhere.' (Country Life, 9 Feb. 1956).

McGRATH (raised caps.) 10″ 1871
Standing, facing right, coloured black.
Pair to 149a ('Pretender').

149. 'PRETENDER' (dates unknown)

A light-brown greyhound, belonging to Mr Punchard; beaten by 'McGrath' in the Waterloo Cup of 1871.

a PRETENDER (raised caps.) 10″ 1871
Standing, facing left, coloured red.
Pair to 148a ('McGrath').

(8) CRIME

150. DICK TURPIN (1706–39)

Highwayman. In 1735, he and Tom King stole a horse in Epping Forest and brought it to White-chapel, where a constable was on the point of arresting King when Turpin rode up and fired. He missed the Constable, but hit King and killed him. He escaped to Yorkshire, but four years later was arrested for horse-stealing, and hanged at York.

The story of Turpin and King was popularised by Harrison Ainsworth's novel, Rookwood (1834), and subsequently by many plays and ballads.

a   DICK TURPIN (raised caps.) $11\frac{1}{2}''$
On horse facing right. In cocked hat (athwart-ships), long coat, breeches, and knee-boots. A pistol in his right hand.
Pair to 151a (King).

b   DICK / TURPIN (raised caps.) $9\frac{1}{4}''$
Almost the same design as (a), but the title in two lines.
Pair to 151b (King).

c   DICK . TURPIN (raised caps.) $11''$
Standing, in cocked hat (athwartships), lace collar, long coat, and knee-boots. Right hand holding a mug against his chest.
Pair to 151d (King).

151. TOM KING (?–1735)

Highwayman; associate of Turpin (q.v.)

a   TOM KING (raised caps.) $11\frac{3}{4}''$
On horse facing left. In tricorn hat, long coat, breeches, and gaiters. A pistol in his right hand.
Pair to 150a (Turpin).

b   TOM / KING (raised caps.) $9\frac{1}{4}''$
Almost the same design as (a), but the title is in two lines.
Pair to 150b (Turpin).

c   T KING (raised caps.) $9\frac{1}{2}''$
Almost as (a), but large ermine cuffs to his coat.
No pair of Turpin has yet been found.

d   TOM KING (raised caps.) $10\frac{1}{2}''$
Standing, in tricorn hat, long coat, and calf-boots with turn-overs. Right hand holds a mug against his chest.
Pair to 150c (Turpin).

152. FRANK GARDINER (1830–c. 1890)

Australian bushranger, born at Goulburn, N.S.W.; in 1862, after two convictions for horse-stealing, joined a gang who held up the gold escort from Forbes, N.S.W., and stole some boxes. £1000 was offered for his arrest, and in 1864 he was captured, tried at Sidney, and sentenced to thirty-two years' imprisonment.

a   FRANK GARDINER (gilt script)   Pl. 52
$9\frac{1}{4}''$ c. 1864
The same model as 150b (Turpin) except for the title.

153. JEMMY WOOD (1756–1836)

A Gloucester draper who kept a bank at the back of his little shop in Westgate, and left £781,007. Four executors immediately propounded a Will dated 1834 by which they divided his estate between them, but a charred fragment of a Codicil, leaving £200,000 to the City of Gloucester, was sent by some unknown person to a Mr Helps who would also benefit from it. Legal proceedings, starting in the Prerogative Court of Canterbury, and ending in the House of Lords, lasted from 1837 to 1844, and aroused great public interest by the many scandalous and ridiculous details of Jemmy's conduct which came to light. Eventually the Corporation of Gloucester, having spent nearly £8000 on the proceedings, got nothing, because they could only receive the money as Trustees, and the Codicil gave no indications of the purposes of the Trust.

a   JEMMY WOOD (raised caps.) $11''$ c. 1845
Standing bare-headed, with a great paunch. Closely resembles his woodcut portrait in *Life and Anecdotes of Jemmy Wood* (Kent & Co. n.d.), probably published in 1845.

b   JIMMY WOOD (script caps.)   Pl. 48
$7\frac{1}{2}''$ c. 1845
Standing, as in (a).

CRIME

154. WILLIAM SMITH O'BRIEN
(1803–64)

M.P. for County Limerick who, in 1848, started an abortive revolution in rural districts of Ireland, was convicted of High Treason, and sentenced to be hanged, drawn, and quartered, but was transported to Tasmania. In 1854 he was pardoned.

a S O'BRIEN (indented caps.) 7″ 1848 **Pl. 7**
Sitting, bare-headed, in handcuffs.
    Pair to 115a (Mrs O'Brien).

b NO TITLE 9″
Standing, bare-headed, in open-necked shirt, short trousers, and bare-feet. Handcuffed. Left forearm on a draped pedestal.
    Note. His hair, in the same style as (a), and the handcuffs make it probable that this is O'Brien.

155. MRS O'BRIEN (dates unknown)

Lucy, daughter of Joseph Gabbett, of Limerick

a MRS O'BRIEN (indented caps.) **Pl. 7**
7½″ 1848
Rising from a chair, and facing half-left, with a shawl over her head.
    Pair to 154a (O'Brien).

156. JAMES BLOMFIELD RUSH
(c. 1800–49)

Owner of Potash Farm, near Wymondham, which was mortgaged to the Recorder of Norwich, Isaac Jermy, of Stanfield Hall, about one mile from the farm, for £5000. Jermy gave notice to foreclose on 30th November 1848, but at about 8 p.m. on the 28th Rush walked across to the Hall, shot Jermy and his son dead and wounded his daughter-in-law and a maidservant. Previously he had forged Jermy's signature to a document by which Jermy gave him absolute ownership of the farm. Rush's trial at Norwich lasted six days; he refused legal aid, but cross-examined witnesses at great length, and himself spoke for fourteen hours. He was hanged on the bridge over the moat of Norwich Castle on 21 April 1849.

a JAMES B RUSH (gilt script) **Pl. 48**
10″ 1849
Standing, bare-headed. A speech in his right hand.
    Pair to 157a (Sandford).

157. EMILY SANDFORD (dates?)

About two years before the murder Rush, a widower with nine children, advertised in The Times *for a governess, and Emily and her parents were so much struck by his 'polite behaviour, apparent respectability, general intelligence, and moral and religious conversation' that she left London for Potash Farm. There he seduced her, having promised to marry her if she bore a child. When he was convicted, largely on her evidence of his words and movements, the Judge, in passing sentence, remarked that 'if you had performed your promise to that unfortunate girl to make her your wife, the policy of the law, that seals the lips of a wife in any proceeding against her husband, might have prevented the appearance of a material witness against you.'*

a EMILY SANDFORD (gilt script) **Pl. 48**
9½″ 1849
Standing, a shawl over her head. A speech in her left hand.
    Pair to 156a (Rush).

158. STANFIELD HALL

A large mansion in a pseudo-Tudor style, surrounded by a moat. Potash Farm, a much smaller building, had many features (three stories, projecting porch, the number and positions of the windows) roughly corresponding with the Hall's, but their comparative sizes are misrepresented to make the figures pair. Engravings in W. Teignmouth Shore's Trial of James Blomfield Rush *(1928) show that their features are fairly accurately represented.*

a STANFIELD HALL (gilt script) **Pl. 49**
8″ 1849
The bridge over the moat is at the right end; actually it was straight in front of the porch.
    Pair to 159a (Potash Farm).

b STANFIELD HALL (gilt script) 7″ 1849
As (a), but (1) there is no projecting porch, and on each side of the door a round column runs up to a pinnacle above the eaves; (2) the chimneys are very high, and resemble clustered columns; (3) a broad path leads straight down from the door; (4) there is no annexe or moat.

159. POTASH FARM

a POTASH FARM (gilt script) 8½″ 1849 **Pl. 49**
    Pair to 158a (Stanfield Hall).
    Note. There are smaller figures of both

buildings with minor differences. One of the Hall, 5¼″, is wrongly titled POTASH FARM, and one of the Farm (see *Country Life*, 5 Dec. 1952) as STANFIELD HALL. Some are untitled.

160. FREDERICK GEORGE MANNING
(1800?–49)

In 1847 Manning, landlord of the White Hart Hotel, Taunton, married at St James's, Piccadilly, Marie de Roux, a native of Lausanne, who was maid to a daughter of the Duke of Sutherland at Stafford (now Lancaster) House. In 1849 they settled at 3 Miniver Place, Bermondsey, and on August 9th she invited their friend (and her lover), Patrick O'Connor, to dinner. They murdered him, and buried him in a hole they had previously made under the kitchen floor. In the next two days Mrs Manning twice visited O'Connor's lodgings, and stole some railway scrip and money which had belonged to him. They were tried at the Old Bailey, and hanged on the roof of Horsemonger Lane Gaol in the presence of a vast mob on November 13th. That evening Dickens, who had watched from a house where he had paid 10 gns. for five tickets, wrote his protest against public executions to The Times.

a F. G. MANNING (gilt script) 9½″ 1849 **Pl. 48**
Standing, bare-headed. A paper (his confession?) in his left hand.
Pair to 161a (M. Manning).

161. MARIA MANNING (1821–49)
See 160 (*F. G. Manning*)

a MARIA MANNING (gilt script) **Pl. 48**
9″ 1849
Standing, in poke bonnet. A handkerchief in her right hand.
Pair to 160a (F. G. Manning).

162. WILLIAM PALMER (1824–56)
Member of the Royal College of Surgeons, and at one time house-surgeon at St Bartholomew's. Later, as General Practitioner at Rugeley, Staffs, took to breeding race-horses. He poisoned his wife in 1854, his brother in August 1855, and his friend, John Parsons Cook, in December 1855. He was convicted at the Old Bailey of the murder of Cook, and hanged in June 1856.

a WILLIAM PALMER (raised caps.) **Pl. 48**
11¼″ 1856
Standing, bare-headed. His left hand on a fence.

163. PALMER'S HOUSE
An accurate representation of William Palmer's house in High Street, Rugeley, separated by a narrow forecourt and railings from the street (see the engraving in The Times Report of the Trial of William Palmer, *Ward & Lock, 1856).*

a PALMER'S HOUSE (raised caps.) **Pl. 49**
7¾″ 1856
A plain, double-fronted, two-storied house, with five windows and two square chimneys.

164. ARTHUR ORTON (1834–98)
'The Tichborne Claimant'. Son of a butcher in Wapping, he emigrated to Australia in 1852, but in 1866 returned at the invitation of Lady Tichborne, widow of the 10th Baronet, who had been convinced by descriptions of him that he was her long-lost eldest son who was presumed to have been drowned in 1854. She recognised him on his arrival, and in 1871 he brought a suit for ejectment against the 12th Baronet, a boy of five. After a trial lasting 102 days he was non-suited, and arrested for perjury. In 1873 he was brought to trial, and after 188 days' hearing sentenced to fourteen years penal servitude. He was released after ten years, and died in poverty.

a SIR . R . TICHBORNE (raised caps.) **Pl. 50**
14¾″ c. 1873
Standing, in top-hat. A gun in his right hand, a bird in his left.

(9) MISCELLANEOUS

1. CONTEMPORARY

165. JAMES BRAIDWOOD (1800–61)

Superintendent of the London Fire-engine Establishment, run by the chief Insurance Companies, from 1832 to 1861. Killed by a falling wall in the Great Fire of Tooley Street. For his funeral the bells of every City church boomed slowly throughout the day, every shop was closed, and the procession was 1½ miles long.

a   BRAIDWOOD (raised caps.)   15"
Standing, in fireman's helmet, coat with epaulettes and trousers. Right hand on a fluted pedestal.
   Illustrated in G. V. Blackstone's *History of the British Fire Service* (1957).

166. GRACE DARLING (1815–42)

Daughter of the lighthouse keeper on the Farne Islands, off the coast of Northumberland. In 1838 she and her father rescued four men and a woman from the wreck of the steamer Forfarshire. Four years later she died of consumption.

a   GRACE DARLING (gilt script)   7"
Two people in a small boat, both facing right. Grace kneels in the stern with her hands raised and clasped; a man sits in the bows. Behind them a rocky coast, with a lighthouse in the centre, and a cottage to the left. The cottage has only a door on the ground floor, and two windows on the first floor, with a straight roof-edge above them.

b   GRACE DARLING (gilt script)   6½"   **Pl. 49**
As (a) but Grace sits in the stern and faces the man, and the cottage has both door and window on the ground floor, and only one window, centred, above, with a curved roof over it.

167. MR ROBERT EVANS (? dates)

In size and style, in features, stance, and all details of clothing, and in the design of its pedestal, this figure very closely resembles the figure of Palmer, the Rugeley poisoner (see Plate 48), and is likely to be of approximately the same date, 1856. No Robert Evans appears to have been in any way connected with Palmer's trial.

In all the usual works of reference there is no record of any Robert Evans who was at all known to the public except the Ven. Robert Wilson Evans who became Archdeacon of Westmorland in 1856. He was then sixty-seven years old, and is unlikely to have been represented with the same figure and black hair as Palmer, who was thirty-two. Actually, in the undated engraving of him by Joseph Brown (see his Bishopric of Souls, 5th ed., 1877) his hair is very sparse, and apparently white. Neither the clothes nor the flowered waistcoat suggest an ecclesiastic, nor does the title 'Mr'. Till 1856 he had been a country clergyman, and his only claim to public interest was his authorship of The Rectory of Valehead (1830), which went through twelve editions but had not been reprinted since 1842.

a   Mᴿ ROBERT EVANS (raised caps.)   11½" c. 1856
Standing, bare-headed, in cravat, long coat, waistcoat, and trousers. His right hand holding a scroll against his chest, and his left on a fluted pedestal.
   Illustrated in *Country Life*, 2 Dec. 1957.

168. MRS AMELIA BLOOMER (1818–94)

Born in New York; a pioneer of the Women's Rights movement. In 1849 advocated a reformed style of dress for women, with a short skirt above loose trousers gathered round the ankles, popularly known as 'Bloomers', and in 1851 came to England, where she had an hilarious welcome. By November a play about her was running at the Adelphi. There were also Bloomer Polkas, Quadrilles, Schottisches, and Waltzes, and a song 'I want to be a Bloomer'.

a   BLOOMERS (indented caps.)   9½"   1851   **Pl. 46**
Standing, in a broad-brimmed and plumed hat, worn on the back of her head, a long coat buttoned at the neck, and 'Bloomers'. An umbrella in her left hand.

A lithograph music cover of 'The Bloomer Polka' (D'Almaine & Co, London, 1851) shows her in similar clothes.

b BLOOMERS (indented caps.) 10″ 1851 **Pl. 46**
A more masculine version of (a). The hat is on top of her head, and has no plume; she has a man's collar and bow tie; her left hand holds a cigar instead of an umbrella.

A lithograph music cover of 'The Bloomer Quadrille' (Musical Bouquet Office, London, 1851) shows her in similar clothes.

169. ROGER GILES (? dates)

'ROGER GILES Surgin, Parish Clerk and Sculemaster, Groser and Hundertaker respectfully informs ladys and gentlemans that he drors teef without waiting a minute, applies laches every hour, blisters on the lowest terms, and vissicks for a penny a peace. . . . Young ladies and gentlemen larnes their grammur and langeudge in the purtiest manner, also grate care taken off their morrels and spelling. . . . Old rags bort and sold here and nowhere else, new laid eggs by me Roger Giles. . . . P. S. I tayches geography, ritmitmetic, cowsticks, jimnastics, and other cheynees tricks.'

(From a cutting from an unidentified newspaper of recent date. The whole advertisement appears in S. Baring-Gould's *The Vicar of Morwenstow*, 1876, but with the omission of 'new laid eggs by me Roger Giles', which is the subject of this improper figure.)

a ROGER / GILES (indented caps.) 5″ **Pl. 48**
Squatting, in round hat, with bare backside.
Note. Mr Burton, of the Curiosity Shop, Falmouth, had this figure made, and sold many as Cornish souvenirs.

170. SHAH NASR-ED-DIN (1829–96)

An able and cultured Shah of Persia who visited England in 1873, and was brilliantly entertained, especially by the Prince of Wales. The public was thrilled by him, and 'Have you seen the Shah?', the title of a song sung by the Great Vance, became a popular catchword. In 1896 he was assassinated in Teheran.

a .HAVE.YOU.SEEN.THE.SHAH. (raised caps.)
13½″ 1873 **Pl. 33**
On horse facing left. In a high fez-shaped hat with a jewelled plume.

171. THE BAND OF HOPE

The first temperance organisation for children, founded at Leeds in 1847 for children who had taken the pledge. In 1851 the local Bands were gathered into a Band of Hope Union.

a BAND OF HOPE (raised caps.) 14″ **Pl. 8**
Hope, standing, bare-headed, with a shield over her left arm, between a kilted child, holding a square flag, and a tree-trunk with a serpent coiled round it.
Note. The figure in Plate 8 is from a 10″ version.

b BAND / OF / HOPE (raised caps.) 10″ **Pl. 8**
Two children standing, in short skirts, and a third sitting between them, in a long skirt, beneath a watch-holder surmounted by two flags bearing the title.

c BAND / OF / HOPE (raised caps.) 6″
Two little girls, in plumed hats and short skirts, holding up a plaque inscribed with the title.

172. THE INDEPENDENT ORDER OF GOOD TEMPLARS

A society of abstainers founded in 1851 at Utica in New York State, with the object of abolishing alcoholic drink throughout the world. Introduced into Great Britain in 1868.

a FAITH / HOPE / AND / CHARITY (on the pedestal). THE GOOD TEMPLARS MOTTO (on the base). (Both in raised caps.) 15½″
Three women standing, bare-headed, in long dresses; the middle one, holding an anchor, on a square pedestal. The woman on the right carries a child, the woman on the left holds up an open book.

b I O G T (raised caps.) 11¼″ 187– **Pl. 8**
Three officials of the Order sitting at a table with its cloth inscribed I O G T. In the centre, behind the table, a bearded man. On each side a woman in a hat in the style of the 1870's (cf. 12a, Pss Louise). All three wear scarves, the man's inscribed W.G.T., and the women's R.H.S. and L.H.S.

173. FOUNTAIN 1861

The Temperance Societies were much disturbed by Gladstone's Refreshment House Act of 1860 which enabled beer licences to be granted to eating houses, and by his Revenue Act of 1861 which reduced the duties on wines. In 1861 the Societies were very active in propaganda, and in installing public drinking fountains.

a FOUNTAIN / 1861 (raised caps.) 15″ 1861
A girl, standing on a high pedestal, in long

dress and shawl. To her right a young man in civilian dress holds up a mug into which she pours from a jug. To her left a woman standing in a low hat and long dress.

174. WINDSOR CASTLE

a NO TITLE 6″   **Pl. 28**
Arched entrance up a flight of steps, with a large three-storied tower on the left, and two smaller towers on the right.
    There is a porcelain figure, 5½″, of the same design inscribed 'Windsor Castle' (gilt script).

175. BALMORAL CASTLE
Built by Queen Victoria 1852–4

a BALMORAL CASTLE (raised caps.) 9¼″ **Pl. 28**
See Pl. 28.

176. BEAUMARIS CASTLE
Founded in 1293 by Edward I, now an ivied ruin

a BEAUMARIS CASTLE (raised caps.) 6¼″
A high arched gateway, with a window and battlements above it; a high tower on the left, a low one on the right.

177. TRINITY COLLEGE, CAMBRIDGE

a TRINITY COLLEGE (raised caps.) 8″
Above a flight of steps a Gothic doorway, flanked by two smaller doors, with two stories and battlements above. On each side a hexagonal tower.
    Roughly based on the east front of the Great Gate.

2. HISTORICAL

178. KING JOHN (1167–1216)

a NO TITLE 12½″
King John, sitting in a tent, crowned, and with both hands on a document (Magna Carta). At each side a page standing, with a flag above him.

179. KING HENRY V (1387–1422)

a HENRY . V . TRYING / ON THE CROWN (raised caps.) 13¾″
Standing, in long tunic. Placing the Crown on his head with both hands (*Henry the Fourth*, Part II, Act iv, sc. 5).

180. KING HENRY VIII (1491–1547) & ANNE BOLEYN (1507–36)

a NO TITLE 10″
The King standing, with Anne on his right. Holding her left hand with his right hand.
    From a music cover by Brandard, entitled 'Henry VIII presenting Ann Boleyn to his Court'.

181. KING CHARLES I (1600–49) & OLIVER CROMWELL (1599–1658)

a K CHARLES & CROMWELL (gilt script) 15″
The King sitting, Cromwell standing, both in broad-brimmed plumed hats, short coats, breeches, and high boots.

182. KING WILLIAM III (1650–1702)

a WILLIAM III 1690 / DERRY AUGHRIM ENNISKILLEN / AND THE BOYNE (gilt script) 14¾″
On horse facing right. In plumed hat, long coat, and high boots. His left hand holding his sword, pointing forward, over the horse's head.

b KING : WILLIAM III (raised caps.)   **Pl. 17**
10¼″
On horse facing left. In plumed hat, long coat, and knee-boots. Long tapering saddle-cloth.
    Pair to 183a (Q. Mary).

c KING WILLIAM 3RD (gilt script) 11¾″
Almost same design as (b), but with short square saddle-cloth.

d KING WM 3 (gilt script) 9¼″
Almost same design as (b).

183. QUEEN MARY (1662–94)
Elder daughter of James II; married William of Orange in 1677

a QUEEN : MARY (raised caps.) 10¼″   **Pl. 17**
On horse facing right. In plumed hat with long veil.
    Pair to 182b (K. William).

MISCELLANEOUS

184. BENJAMIN FRANKLIN (1706-90)

Born at Boston, Mass.; apprenticed to a printer. Sent to England on a political mission in 1757. For some years tried to reconcile the Colonies with Great Britain, but later negotiated the alliance between the Colonies and France.

a   FRANKLIN (raised caps.)   14″   Pl. 14
Standing, bare-headed. A tricorn hat in his left hand, a document in his right. Angular base.

185. GEORGE WASHINGTON (1732-99)

a   WASHINGTON (raised caps.)   15½″
Same design as 184a (Franklin).

b   GENERAL WASHINGTON (gilt script)   Pl. 14
15½″
Same as (a), but on a circular base.
Copies are also found inscribed THE OLD ENGLISH GENTLEMAN (gilt script). A traditional song of this title, rewritten by Charles H. Purday in 1826, was still popular in the 1850's; editions of that period have lithograph fronts of an old gentleman in this costume.
Note. All recorded Victorian figures of Washington have Franklin's head, and all of Franklin and Washington have the same body. In the Metropolitan Museum, New York, there is a figure made by Enoch Wood *c.* 1800 with that body but with Washington's head. Wood is said to have also made a standing figure of Franklin (Wedgwood & Ormsbee, *Staffordshire Pottery*, Macbride, New York, 1947) which may have been the original of all the Victorian figures of both of them. In all the pieces known to me the Washington is larger than the Franklin.

186. LORD EDWARD FITZGERALD
(1763-98)

Son of the 1st Duke of Leinster. In 1796 joined the United Irishmen, and headed a Committee to co-operate with a French invasion of Ireland. In 1798 was wounded while being arrested by the Dublin police, and died of his wounds.

a   LORD EDWARD FITZGERALD (gilt script)
14″ 1898   Pl. 17
Standing, bare-headed, in short coat and trousers. Left hand on a pedestal inscribed WHO FEARS TO SPEAK OF '98 / 1798 1898 (transfer caps.).
Same series as 187a (McCracken) and 188a (Tone).

187. HENRY JOY McCRACKEN (1767-98)

Helped to form the first United Irishmen, in Belfast in 1791. In 1798 commanded the rebels in Co. Antrim, and was tried and executed.

a   HENRY JOY McCRACKEN (gilt script)   Pl. 17
14″ 1898
Standing, bare-headed, in short coat, breeches, and stockings. Left hand on pedestal inscribed as in 186a (Fitzgerald).
Same series as 186a (Fitzgerald) and 188a (Tone).

188. THEOBALD WOLFE TONE
(1763-98)

In 1791 helped to found the United Irishmen in Dublin. In 1796 was Adjutant-General in the French expedition to Ireland which failed to land. A second expedition surrendered at sea, and he was sentenced to death, but committed suicide.

a   THEOBALD WOLFE TONE (gilt script)   Pl. 17
14″ 1898
Standing, bare-headed, in military jacket, breeches and stockings. Left hand holds two flags across his chest. To his right a pedestal inscribed as in 186a (Fitzgerald).
Same series as 186a (Fitzgerald) and 187a (McCracken).

189. RICHARD WHITTINGTON
(d. 1423)

Son of Sir William Whittington, of Gloucestershire. Thrice Mayor of London. Married Alice, daughter of Sir Ivo Fitzwaryn. Very rich, and a great benefactor of the City. The legend of his poverty, his cat, etc., first appeared in a play of 1605.

a   DICK WHITTINGTON (raised caps.)   17″
Standing, in hat, cape, coat, breeches, and stockings, a belt with a wallet round his waist. A bundle and stick in his left hand, his right hand on a milestone inscribed IV / MILES / TO / LONDON (raised u. & l. case).

190. OLD PARR (1483?-1635)

Thomas Parr, of Alderbury, Salop. Said to have gone into service in 1500, and to have done penance for incontinence at the age of 105. In 1635 the Earl of Arundel brought him to Charles I's Court, and he soon died.
'Old Parr's Life Pills' were much advertised in mid-Victorian times.

MISCELLANEOUS

a OLD PARR (gilt script) 9½″   **Pl. 47**
Standing, bare-headed and bearded, in a long
cloak, with a basket of vegetables on his left
arm.

191. WILLIAM WALLACE (1272–1305)

*Scottish hero. Drove the English out of Scotland
in 1297, but in 1298 was defeated by Edward I at
Falkirk. From 1303 conducted guerilla warfare in
Scotland, but in 1305 was betrayed, brought to
London, tried in Westminster Hall, and executed.*

a WALLACE (raised caps.) 17½″
Standing, leaning slightly to his left, in Scottish costume, with plaid over his left shoulder.
Round shield on his left arm; sword in his
right hand.

b WALLACE (gilt script) 15½″
Standing, in full Scottish costume, his plaid
over both shoulders, and sword in his right
hand.
   192a (Bruce) is the same figure, with the
title changed.

192. ROBERT BRUCE (1274–1329)

*King of Scotland. In 1296 paid homage to
Edward I, but rebelled in 1297. In 1314 defeated
Edward II at Bannockburn. In 1328 made peace
with Edward III.*

a BRUCE (gilt script) 15½″
Same figure as 191b (Wallace).

193. ROB ROY (1671–1734)

*Robert Macgregor or Campbell, a Highland free-
booter. He was captured in 1728, and sentenced, but
was pardoned and became a peaceful citizen.*

a ROB ROY (raised caps.) 19″
Standing, in full Scottish costume, plaid over
his left shoulder. An octagonal shield, decorated with thistles, on his left arm.
   Pair to 194a (Tell).

b ROB ROY (raised caps.) 13½″
Standing, much inclined to his right, in full
Scottish costume, plaid over his right
shoulder. Round shield behind his left forearm; sword in his right hand.

c NO TITLE 11″
As (b), but no sporran. Dirk instead of sword
in his right hand, and a horn slung from his
left shoulder.

d NO TITLE ? height.
As (b), but upright, and the round shield,
decorated with a thistle, in front of his left
forearm.
   Illustrated in *Connaissance des Arts*, No. 51,
May 1956, but height not stated.

194. WILLIAM TELL

The legendary Swiss hero

a W^M TELL (raised caps.) 18¾″
Standing, in plumed bonnet, short-skirted
dress, and calf-high boots. His bow against
his right side.
   Pair to 193a (Rob Roy).

b WILLIAM TELL (gilt script) 10¼″
Standing, in high-plumed bonnet, short-
skirted dress, a cape over both shoulders and
fastened at his neck. On his right a small
child, holding an apple.

A NOTE ON RARITIES

This list includes the more important portrait figures of contemporaries which appear to be very rare; it does not include the historical figures because they are generally of less interest to collectors. Many in the list are the only known models of their subjects. Of some of them only one copy is known, and of most of them only a very few. With the kind assistance of other collectors it has been possible to reproduce all of these, except Sir George Cathcart, Ben Caunt, James Braidwood and Mr Robert Evans, in this book.

ROYAL
D. of Edinburgh (**Pl. 15**)
Dss of Edinburgh (**Pl. 15**)
Pss Alice (**Pl. 52**)
P. Louis of Hesse (**Pl. 52**)
Pss Louise (**Pl. 5**)
Marquess of Lorne (**Pl. 5**)
George, D. of Cambridge (**Pl. 23**)
K. Leopold (**Pl. 20**)
D. of Clarence (**Pl. 50**)

STATESMEN
O'Connell (**Pl. 2**)
T. S. Duncombe (**Pl. 47**)
Lord Shaftesbury (**Pl. 7**)
Parnell (**Pl. 51**)

NAVAL & MILITARY
Sir R. Sale (**Pl. 32**)
Lady Sale (**Pl. 32**)
Sir J. Franklin (**Pl. 46**)
Lady Franklin (**Pl. 46**)
Napoleon III (**Pl. 20**)
Empress Eugénie (**Pl. 20**)
Lord Raglan (**Pl. 19**)

Sir J. Simpson (**Pl. 24**)
Sir G. Cathcart 47Aa
Sir C. Windham (**Pl. 24**)
Sir W. Codrington (**Pl. 27**)
Sir de L. Evans (**Pl. 27**)
Sir W. F. Williams (**Pl. 23**)
Miss Nightingale (**Pl. 31**)
Marshal Saint-Arnaud (**Pl. 26**)
Genl Canrobert (**Pl. 27**)
John Brown (**Pl. 33**)
Abraham Lincoln (**Pl. 34**)
P. Fredk. Charles (**Pl. 37**)
Marshal Bazaine (**Pl. 37**)
Marshal MacMahon (**Pl. 37**)

RELIGIOUS
Rev. Christmas Evans (**Pl. 40**)
Rev. John Elias (**Pl. 39**)
Dr Raffles (**Pl. 39**)
Cooke, D.D. (**Pl. 39**)
Pope Pius IX (**Pl. 41**)
Cardl. Manning (**Pl. 41**)
Dr E. M. Goulburn (**Pl. 51**)
Genl. Booth (**Pl. 4**)
C. H. Spurgeon (**Pl. 43**)

STAGE
William Macready (**Pl. 47**)
Luigi Lablache (**Pl. 52**)
Edward Morgan (**Pl. 52**)
Van Amburgh (**Pl. 48**)
Jullien (**Pl. 7**)
Jenny Lind (**Pl. 44**)
J. S. Rarey (**Pl.52**)

SPORT
Ben Caunt 140a
Fuller Pilch (**Pl. 52**)
Thomas Box (**Pl. 52**)
Capt. Webb (**Pl. 48**)

CRIME
Frank Gardiner (**Pl. 52**)
W. Smith O'Brien (**Pl. 7**)
Mrs O'Brien (**Pl. 7**)

MISCELLANEOUS
James Braidwood 165a
Mr Robert Evans 167a
Mrs Bloomer (**Pl. 46**)
'Have you seen the Shah?' (**Pl. 33**)

Contemporary copies of all the Shakespearean figures made by the 'Tallis' factory are very hard to find, especially in their larger sizes.

Index

*The figures in brackets refer to the
entries in the Catalogue (pp. 46–86)*

INDEX

INDEX

INDEX

INDEX

[5.] Prince Albert 2j — Prince Albert 2a — Prince Albert 2k — Queen Victoria 1u — Queen Victoria 1c — Queen Victoria 1t
Marquess of Lorne 13a — Queen Victoria 1e — Prince Albert 2c — Princess Louise 12a

[6.] Queen Victoria 1x — Queen Victoria and Prince Albert 2s — Prince Albert 2l
Prince Albert 2b — Queen Victoria 1v — Prince Albert 2r — Queen Victoria 1d

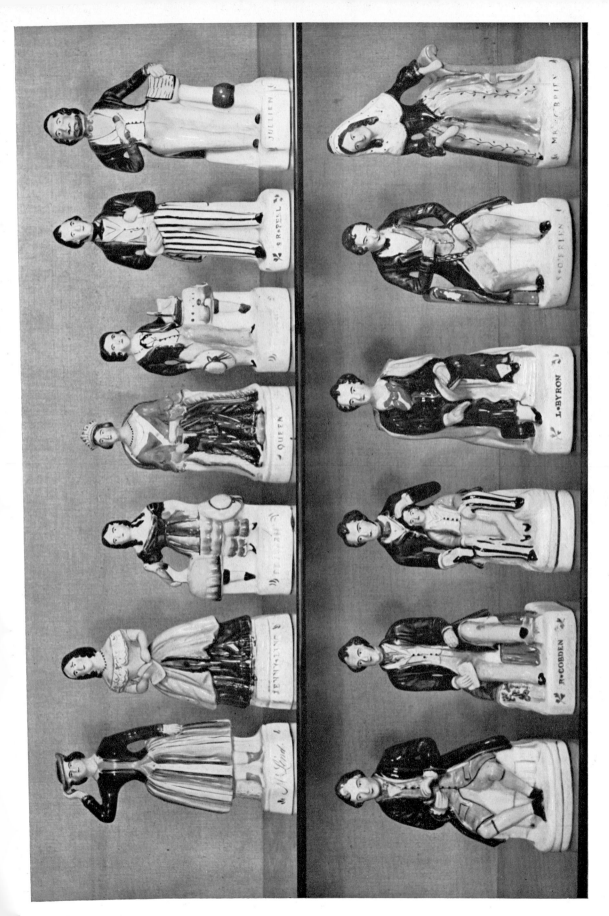

[7.] Jenny Lind 134f — Jenny Lind 134g — Princess Royal 3b — Queen Victoria 1a — Prince of Wales 5b — Peel 22c — Jullien 132a
Burns 118e — Cobden 27a — Shaftesbury 24a — Byron 121a — W. S. O'Brien 154a — Mrs O'Brien 155a

[8.] Prince Albert 2g — Princess Royal and Prince of Wales 3e — Queen Victoria 1m
Band of Hope 171a — Good Templars 172b — Band of Hope 171b

[9.] Prince Frederick William 4a — Princess Royal 3c
Duchess of Cambridge 15a — Duke of Cambridge 15a — Duke of Cambridge 14b — Duke of Cambridge 14a

[10.] Princess Royal and Prince Frederick William 3f — Prince of Wales and Princess 5s

[11.] Prince of Wales 5g — Prince of Wales 5c — Prince of Wales 5d

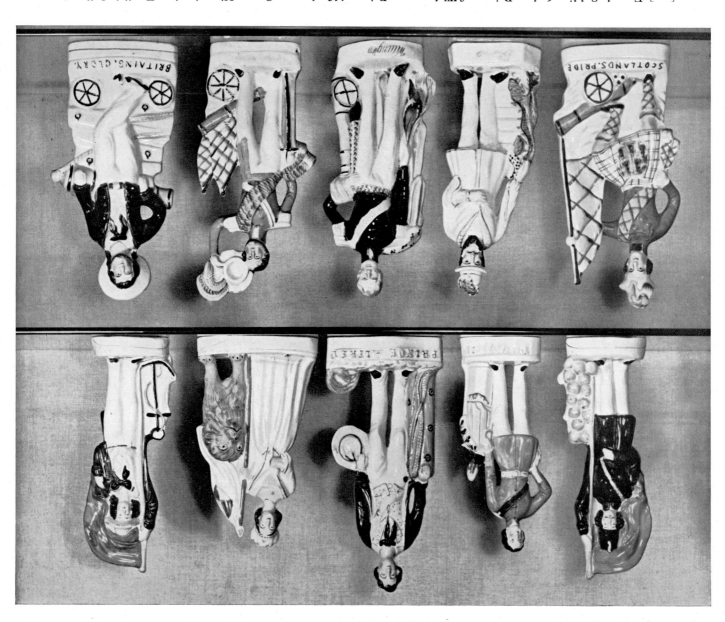

[12.] French Soldier 61d — Prince of Wales 5e — Prince Alfred 7c — Queen Victoria 1j — English Sailor 61c
Scotland's Pride 61b — Kossuth 25c — Wellington 20g — Colin Campbell 62a — Britain's Glory 61a

[13.] Colin Campbell 62d — Havelock 63c
Prince of Wales 5i — Peel 22f — Princess of Wales 6b

[14.] Washington 185a — Benjamin Franklin 184a

Washington's right hand has been incorrectly restored. It should be holding a paper, like Franklin's.

[15.] Prince of Wales 5m — Queen Victoria 1 0 — Duke of Edinburgh 7a — Duchess of Edinburgh 8a

[17.] Queen Mary 183a — King William III 182b

Parnell 30a — Wolfe Tone 188a — McCracken 187a — Lord E. Fitzgerald 186a

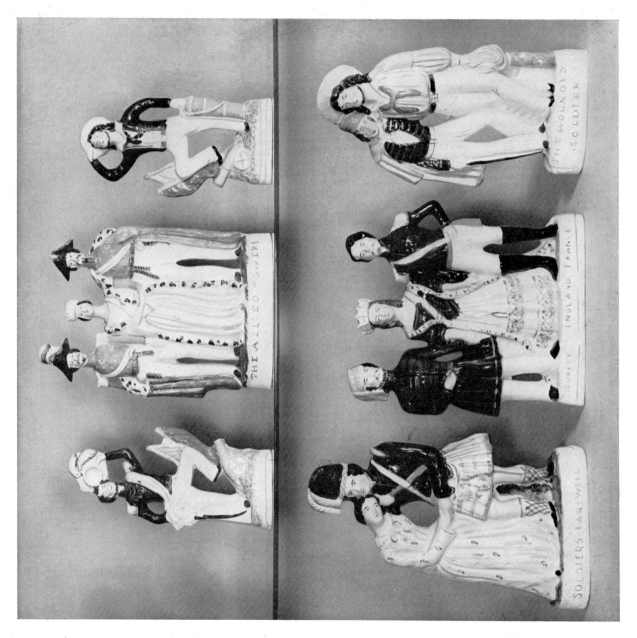

[18.] Scotland 61h — The Allied Powers 1bb — England 61g

Soldier's Farewell 61f — Turkey England France 1cc — Wounded Soldier 61e

[19.] Napoleon III 39a — King of Sardinia 41b — Queen Victoria and King of Sardinia 1z— Lord Raglan 45a

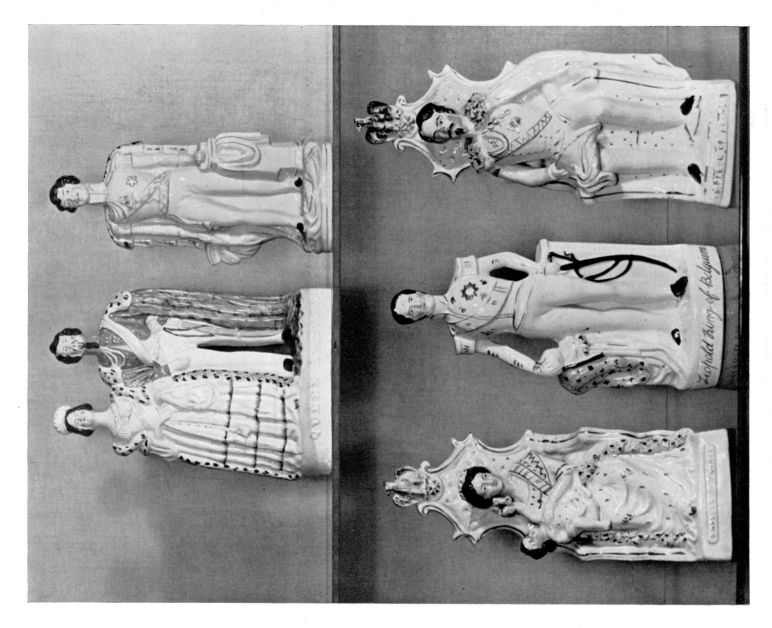

[20.] Queen Victoria and Napoleon III 1y — Prince Albert 2n
Empress Eugénie 40c — King Leopold 17a — Napoléon III 39c

[21.] General Pelissier 55a — Admiral Napier 44b — Admiral Dundas 43a — King of Sardinia 41a

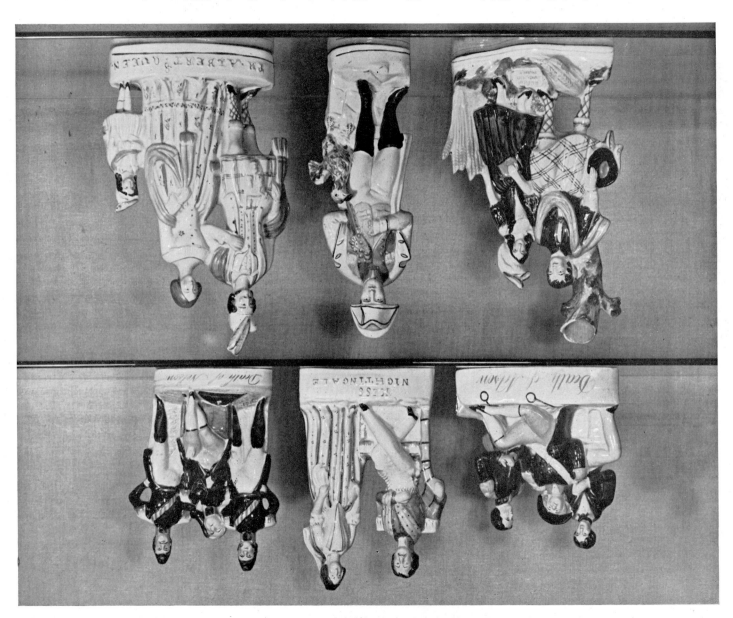

[23.] Sir G. Brown 46b — Sir G. Brown 46c — Duke of Cambridge 16a — Sir W. F. Williams 51a — Sir J. Simpson 47a
Napoleon III 39e — General Pelissier 55d — Empress Eugénie 40a

[24.] Sir J. Simpson 47b — Sir C. Windham 48a

[25.] George Parr (?) 144a — Omar Pasha 56a — Julius Caesar (?) 144b

[26.] Marshal St-Arnaud 53a — Lord Raglan 45b
Omar Pasha 56c — Omar Pasha 56d — The Sultan 42a

[27.] Admiral Napier 44c — General Canrobert 54a — Omar Pasha 56b — Sir W. Codrington 49b — Sir de L. Evans 50a

[28.] Balmoral Castle 175a — Windsor Castle 174a
The Redan 59a — Sebastopol 57a — Malakoff 58a

[29.] The Soldier's Dream 61i — Highland Jessie 64a

[30.] Soldier and Sailor 61j — The Victory 60a

[31.] Havelock 63a — Wellington 20l — Florence Nightingale 52a

[32.] Sir R. Sale 35a — L. E. Landon 122a — Lady Sale 36a
Volunteer Rifles 65a — Florence Nightingale 52c — England and France 61k

[33.] Garibaldi 69e — Garibaldi 69f — John Brown 67a — Garibaldi 69c
Wellington 20o — The Lion Queen 138a — Byron 121b — The Shah 170a — Burns 118f

[34.] Abraham Lincoln 68a
Garibaldi 69i — Colonel Peard 70a

[35.] Queen of Prussia 73a — King of Prussia 72a — Quin 124a — Highland Mary 119a

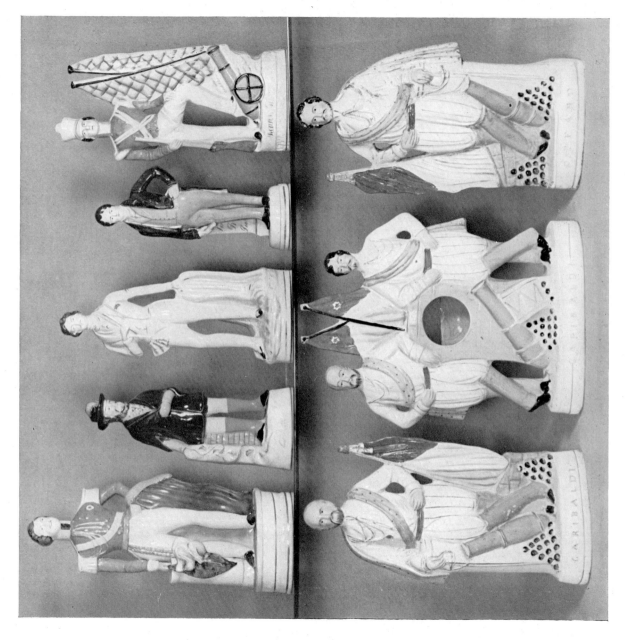

[36.] Prince Albert 2 o — Kossuth 25b — Prince Albert 2m — Peel 22b — Ready Willing 61
Garibaldi 69j — Garibaldi and Colonel Peard 69k — Colonel Peard 70b

[37.] Marshal MacMahon 78a — Marshal Bazaine 77a — King of Prussia 72b
Moltke 76a — Prince Frederick Charles 74a — Bismarck 75a

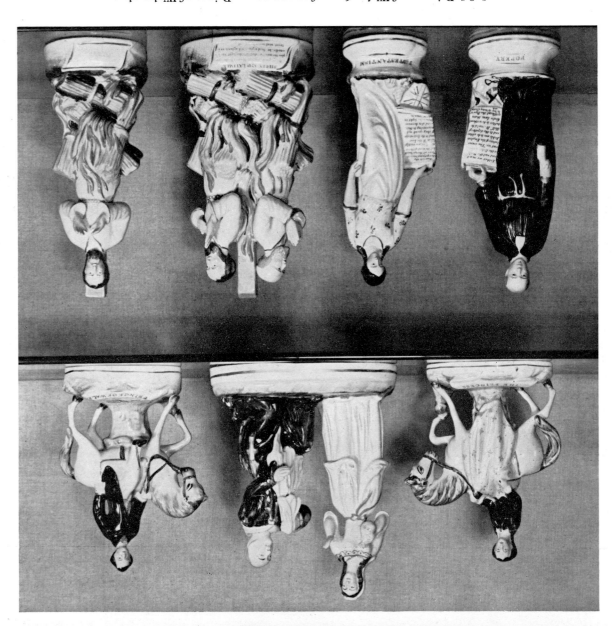

[38.] Princess of Wales 6a — £10,000 94a — Prince of Wales 5b
Popery 92a — Protestantism 93a — Ridley and Latimer 91a — Cranmer 90a

[42.] Sankey 113a — Moody 112a — Gladstone 28b — Beaconsfield 26a

[41.] Pope Pius IX 105a — Sister Hallahan 106a — O'Connell 21b — Père Moulaert 107a — Cardinal Manning 108a

[40.] Rev. Christmas Evans 99a — Gordon 80c — St Vincent de Paul 95a

[39.] Dr Cooke 104a — Dr Raffles 102a — W. O'Bryan 101a — Wesley 97a
Wesley 97b — J. J. Gurney 103a — Rev. J. Elias 100a — Gladstone 28a — Spurgeon 111b

[38.] Princess of Wales 6a — £10,000 94a — Prince of Wales 5h
Popery 92a — Protestantism 93a — Ridley and Latimer 91a — Cranmer 90a

[37.] Marshal MacMahon 78a — Marshal Bazaine 77a — King of Prussia 72b
Moltke 76a — Prince Frederick Charles 74a — Bismarck 75a

[43.] Spurgeon 111a — Scott 120a — Burns 118a — Burns 118b — Admiral Blake 31a

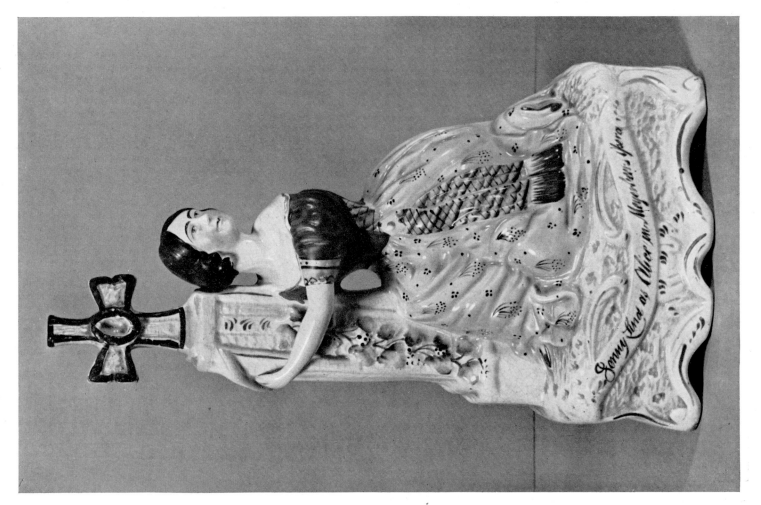

[44.] Jenny Lind 134a

[45.] Ophelia 137a (note) — E. A. Sothern 136a — Shylock 127b — Macbeth 127c — Lady Macbeth 135a — Falstaff 129a
Jenny Lind 134e — Hamlet 126d — Richard III 125a — Jenny Lind 134d

[46.] Bloomers 168b — Jenny Lind 134i — Captain Cook 32a — Jenny Lind 134h — Bloomers 168a
Lady Franklin 38a — Eliza Cook 123a — Voltaire 117a — Peel 22d — Sir J. Franklin 37a
(All except the two of Jenny Lind are from the "Alpha" factory.)

[47.] Old Parr 190a — William Penn 96a — Lord Napier 71a — Macready 127a — T. S. Duncombe 23a
The Grapplers 146a — Van Amburgh 131b — Heenan and Sayers 141a

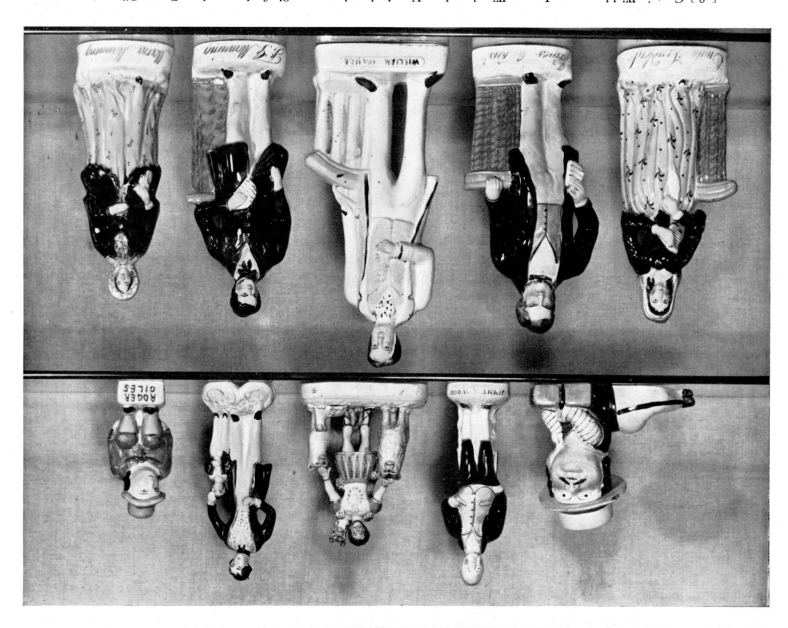

[48.] Captain Webb 145a — Jemmy Wood 153b — Van Amburgh 131a — Shaftesbury 24b — Roger Giles 169a
Emily Sandford 157a — J. B. Rush 156a — William Palmer 162a — F. G. Manning 160a — Maria Manning 161a

[49.] Shakespeare's House 115a — Palmer's House 163a — Grace Darling 166b
Stanfield Hall 158a — Potash Farm 159a

[50.] Duke of Clarence 18a — Gordon 80a — Arthur Orton 164a — Princess May 19a

[51.] Peel 22a — Napoleon III and Eugénie 39g
Dr Goulburn 109a — Parnell 30b

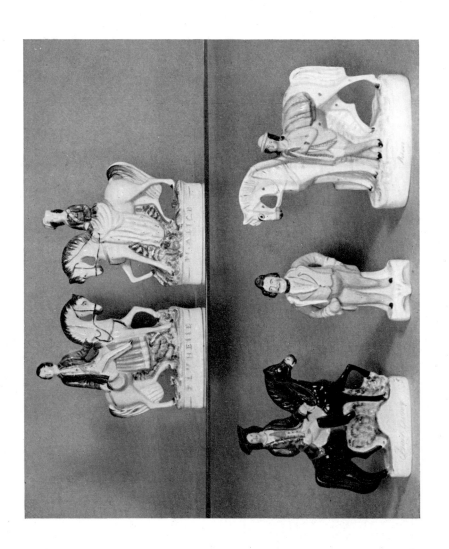

[52.] Prince Louis of Hesse 11a — Princess Alice 10a
Frank Gardiner 152a — Luigi Lablache 128a — Rarey 139a
Thomas Box 143a — Fuller Pilch 142a — Edward Morgan 130a